Haider

GCSE OCR 21st Century
Core Science
The Workbook

This book is for anyone doing **GCSE OCR 21st Century Core Science** at higher level.

It's full of **tricky questions**... each one designed to make you **sweat** — because that's the only way you'll get any **better**.

There are questions to see **what facts** you know. There are questions to see how well you can **apply those facts**. And there are questions to see what you know about **how science works**.

It's also got some daft bits in to try and make the whole experience at least vaguely entertaining for you.

What CGP is all about

Our sole aim here at CGP is to produce the highest quality books — carefully written, immaculately presented and dangerously close to being funny.

Then we work our socks off to get them out to you — at the cheapest possible prices.

Contents

Published by Coordination Group Publications Ltd.

Editors:
Amy Boutal, Ellen Bowness, Tom Cain, Katherine Craig, Sarah Hilton, Kate Houghton,
Rose Parkin, Ami Snelling, Laurence Stamford, Julie Wakeling, Sarah Williams.

Contributors:
Michael Aicken, Mike Bossart, Jane Davies, Mark A Edwards, Adrian Schmit, Paul Warren.

ISBN: 978 1 84146 623 1

With thanks to Barrie Crowther, Ian Francis and Sue Hocking for the proofreading.

With thanks to Jan Greenway for the copyright research.

Photographs on page 3 reproduced with kind permission from Adrian Schmit.

*Data on page 22 reproduced with kind permission from Earth System Research Laboratory,
National Oceanic and Atmospheric Administration, and Scripps Institution of Oceanography,
University of California.*

*Article on page 26 based on information from, "Nino Künzli, Michael Jerrett, Wendy J. Mack,
Bernardo Beckerman, Laurie LaBree, Frank Gilliland, Duncan Thomas, John Peters, and
Howard N. Hodis. Ambient Air Pollution and Atherosclerosis in Los Angeles.
Environmental Health Perspectives 113:201–206 (2005)" with kind permission from the publisher.*

Data on page 29 reproduced courtesy of Haynes Publishing.

Data on page 38 courtesy of NASA/JPL-Caltech.

*Graph on page 43 reproduced with kind permission from the Astronomy Department,
Indiana University.*

*Data on page 49 reproduced with kind permission from the Health Protection Agency,
www.HPA.org.uk.*

Data on page 57 reproduced with kind permission from the British Heart Foundation © 2006.

Data on page 81 © Crown Copyright 1998, data supplied by the Met Office.

Timeline on page 106 reproduced with permission from New Scientist.

Data on page 115 courtesy of NPL, http://www.npl.co.uk © Crown Copyright 2006.

Groovy website: www.cgpbooks.co.uk

Printed by Elanders Hindson Ltd, Newcastle upon Tyne.
Jolly bits of clipart from CorelDRAW®

Based on the classic CGP style created by Richard Parsons.

Genes, Chromosomes and DNA

Q1 Tick the boxes to show whether the following statements are **true** or **false**.

	True	False
a) The nucleus of a cell contains instructions for how an organism develops.	☐	☐
b) Genes are short lengths of chromosomes.	☐	☐
c) Genes are found in chromosomes.	☐	☐
d) There are 23 pairs of genes.	☐	☐
e) Genes are instructions for a cell that describe how to make proteins.	☐	☐

Q2 Some **structures** found in the human body are named below. Add them into the table in order of **size**, from **smallest** to **largest** and then match each structure to its description. One has been done for you.

cell
gene
nucleus
chromosome

smallest
⟶
largest

cell

structure inside a cell where all genetic material is found

structures that come in pairs

the smallest unit of an individual that can function independently

an instruction to tell a cell how to make a protein

Q3 DNA provides **instructions** that tell cells which **proteins** to make.

a) Explain what **structural** proteins are.

....

b) What role do **enzymes** play in the body?

....

c) How can different alleles lead to different characteristics?

....

....

Top Tips: Remember humans have 23 pairs of chromosomes, that's 46 in total. Chromosomes carry genes that provide instructions for cells about how to make different proteins. It's the different proteins that are responsible for all of your characteristics like hair colour and eye colour.

Genes and Variation

Q1 An organism's genes are carried in **chromosomes**.

a) How many chromosomes would you find in a human **skin** cell? ....

b) How many chromosomes would you find in a human **sex** cell? ....

c) How many **copies** of each chromosome would you find in a sex cell? ....

Q2 Explain why **children** tend to resemble both of their **parents** but don't look exactly like either one.

....

....

....

Q3 The diagram below shows the nuclei of two simple organisms that contain only **four pairs** of chromosomes. Different **alleles** are shown using different shades of the same colour.

Organism 1

Organism 2

Organisms 1 and 2 **mate**. Put a tick in the correct boxes to show the nuclei of the cells that could be produced at fertilisation.

Look carefully at the different coloured chromosomes, remember one in each pair must come from each parent.

A

B

C

D

Genes and Variation

Q4 The diagram shows a **pair** of human **chromosomes**. These chromosomes carry a **gene** for **ear lobes**. The position of the gene is marked on one of the chromosomes in the diagram.

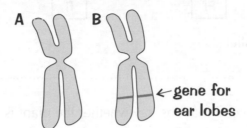

a) Draw the position of the gene for ear lobes on chromosome A.

b) If chromosome A came from the **mother** where must chromosome B have come from?

....

c) Chromosome A contains a **different version** of the ear lobe gene from chromosome B. Underline the correct statement below.

Sex cells contain the instructions for both versions of ear lobe.

Sex cells will only contain the instructions for one version of ear lobe.

Q5 The picture below shows two **brothers**. They have the **same parents** but don't bear a close resemblance to one another.

Complete the following statements by circling the correct word(s) to explain why two brothers (or sisters) can look quite different from each other, even though they have the same parents.

Despite inheriting **half / all / none** of their genes from the same mother and **all / none / half** from the same father, siblings don't look identical. This is because of the way **sex cells / liver cells** are made and the way they **combine / separate**. There are **tens / millions** of different combinations. Every person in the world will have **a unique / the same** combination of alleles — that's why no two people in the world are exactly the same, with the exception of **cousins / identical twins**.

Top Tips: All of this is pretty mind-boggling stuff. It's weird to think you only look the way you do because of lots of random events that took place when you were being created, apart form that dodgy haircut — you've only got yourself to blame for that.

4

Inheritance

Q1 A plant has **two alleles** for **flower colour**. The allele for **violet** flowers **(F)** is **dominant** over the allele for **white** flowers **(f)**. The possible allele combinations are shown below.

FF   Ff   ff

a) Give a definition of the word allele.

....

b) For each of the different allele combinations, say whether the plant is **homozygous** or **heterozygous**.

    i) FF ....

    ii) Ff ....

    iii) ff ....

c) What **colour** flowers would the plants with these alleles have? Circle the correct answer.

    i) FF   violet / white

    ii) Ff   violet / white

    iii) ff   violet / white

Q2 In cats, the allele for black fur **(B)** is **dominant** over the allele for brown fur **(b)**. Two black cats, Jasper and Belle, have a litter of kittens. Most are black, but one is brown. Tick the boxes to show whether the following statements are **true** or **false**.

	True	False
a) All the brown kittens have the alleles bb.	☐	☐
b) Jasper's alleles are BB.	☐	☐
c) Belle's alleles are Bb.	☐	☐
d) The brown kitten must be a mutation — all the kittens should be black.	☐	☐

Q3 Some people can roll their tongue and others can't. The ability tongue roll is controlled by a single gene. **Rolling (R)** is **dominant** to **non-rolling (r)**.

Izzy can roll her tongue but Saaj cannot. What conclusions can you draw about Izzy and Saaj's genetic make-up for the tongue rolling gene? Explain your answer.

....

....

....

Module B1 — You and Your Genes

Inheritance

Q4 Eye colour is controlled by the interaction of several genes. One of these genes determines whether or not a person has **brown** eyes. In this gene, the allele for **brown** eyes (B) is **dominant** over the allele for **blue** eyes (b).

Hector and Alyson are both heterozygous for this gene (Bb) and they are expecting a baby.

a) Based on the expression of this gene, write what colour eyes each offspring could have and say whether they are heterozygous or homozygous.

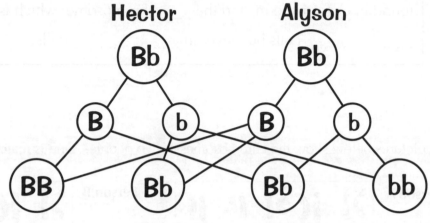

Colour ....

Homozygous /
Heterozygous ....

b) What is the chance that the new baby could have **blue** eyes? Give your answer as a percentage.

....

c) Hector and Alyson already have three children, they all have brown eyes. Hector thinks that this child will definitely have blue eyes. Is Hector right? Explain your answer.

....

....

Q5 In **guinea pigs**, the allele for short hair **(H)** is dominant over the allele for long hair **(h)**.

a) Is it possible for two short haired guinea pigs produce long haired offspring? Explain your answer.

....

b) Is it possible for two long haired guinea pigs produce short haired offspring? Explain your answer.

....

....

....

Would long haired guinea pigs be homozygous or heterozygous?.

Girl or Boy?

Q1 Fill in the gaps in the passage below about how a person's **sex** is determined.

> Everybody has one pair of chromosomes that determine whether they are
> male or female. These chromosomes are called the ....
> chromosomes. There are two types, the .... chromosome, which can be
> found in eggs or sperm, and the .... chromosome, which is found in
> .... cells but never in .... cells.

Q2 The pictures below show the chromosomes of two people. One is **male** and the other is **female**.

Person A 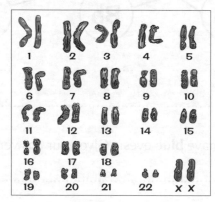 Person B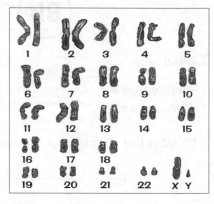

a) Which is **female**? ....

b) How can you tell? ....

Q3 The **genetic diagram** below is incomplete, fill in the spaces to show how **sex** is inherited.

female   **male**

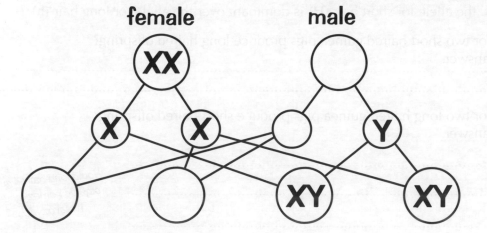

My son Jeremy shall
inherit my stamp
collection and my
chromosomes.

Girl or Boy?

Q4 Mr and Mrs Kowalski have **three sons** and Mrs Kowalski is pregnant with a fourth child. What is the chance of this baby being another boy? Circle the correct answer.

50%   75%   10%   25%

Q5 Read the passage below and then answer the question the follows.

> The sex of a baby is determined by whether its father's sperm cell was carrying an X chromosome or a Y chromosome. On average, half the sperm cells a man produces carry an X chromosome and half carry a Y. You'd expect this to lead to equal numbers of boys and girls being born. However, in one year approximately 600 000 babies born we born in the UK. Amongst these babies, there were 20 000 more boys than girls.

From the list below, tick the boxes next to any reasons that are likely explanations for these figures.

The 50:50 ratio is only a probability and it will always vary to some extent. ☐

The data must be incorrect. ☐

Perhaps the Y sperm have a better chance of fertilising an egg than X ones. ☐

22 000 more girls would've been born the year before so overall the numbers are equal. ☐

The scientific theory that predicts a 50:50 ratio must be wrong. ☐

Q6 The sex of a developing human embryo is controlled by a **gene** that codes for the production of a **protein** called **testis determining factor** (TDF).

a) Explain how TDF controls the sex of a developing embryo.

....

....

....

b) Which chromosome do you think the gene that codes for TDF is found on?

....

Top Tips: Remember the results you get when you draw a genetic diagram are only probabilities, there's an equal chance of having a boy or a girl — though if you're anything like as unlucky as me you'll end up in a house where girls outnumber boys 3:1.

Inheritance and Environment

Q1 Complete the passage using the words provided.

| interaction | single | height | unpredictable | number | thousands |

Characteristics controlled by a .... gene are quite rare. The majority of characteristics depend on a .... of genes working together. Because of the .... between genes there are .... of different combinations, this makes inheritance very .... is an example of a characteristic determined by a combination of genes.

Q2 Put ticks in the appropriate columns in the table below to show if these characteristics are caused by **genes**, the **environment** or **both**.

Variation	Genes	Environment	Both
Height			
Eye colour			
Hairstyle			
Skin colour			
Blood group			

Q3 **Diabetes** is a disease that affects the body's ability to control blood sugar levels. Scientists think that one type is caused by a combination of **genetic** and **environmental** factors. For each of the following statements, explain whether it indicates a genetic or environmental cause or a mixture of the two.

a) If you are an identical twin of someone with diabetes, there's an increased chance you'll also suffer from it.

....

....

....

b) Diabetes is more common in colder places, and is more likely to develop in winter.

....

c) People who were breast-fed as a baby have a reduced chance of getting diabetes.

....

d) Having a parent who has diabetes leads to a slightly higher chance of getting the disease.

....

Module B1 — You and Your Genes

Inheritance and Environment

Q4 Some diseases can be caused by both a person's **genes** and their **environment**. Read the statements about two families, the Greens and the Perkins and answer the questions that follow.

- The Greens and the Perkins live next door to each other.
- For generations, the men in both families have worked in the local paint factory.
- Mr Green has been diagnosed with cancer. His father, who also worked in the factory, died of the same cancer some years ago.
- Mr Perkins and his father are both healthy.
- Mr Green has two brothers who have moved away from the area and have different jobs. Neither man has developed cancer.

a) What evidence is there that Mr Green's cancer has been caused by **genetic** factors?

....

....

b) What evidence is there that Mr Green's cancer been caused by his **environment**?

....

....

c) What would you need to do to get a better idea whether this type of cancer is caused by genes or the environment?

....

....

Q5 The following factors are all known to increase people's **risk** of getting **heart disease**. Tick the boxes to show whether they are usually caused by **genetic** or **environmental** factors.

	Genetic	Environmental
a) Smoking	☐	☐
b) High cholesterol level	☐	☐
c) Being overweight	☐	☐
d) Having a close relative who has died of heart disease	☐	☐
e) A high salt diet	☐	☐

Top Tips: Most things are actually affected by a combination of your genes and the environment you live in, things like health, intelligence and sporting ability. Either way it means that you can blame your parents if you're a bit fat, stupid and rubbish at sport, I know I certainly do.

Module B1 — You and Your Genes

Clones

Q1 Complete the passage below choosing from the words provided.

nucleus growth enucleated dividing physically genetically host egg donor

Clones are .... identical organisms. They can be made by scientists in the laboratory by removing the .... from an .... cell (this forms an .... cell). It is replaced with a nucleus taken from an adult .... cell. The cell is then stimulated to start .... The embryo that results from this is .... identical to the .... cell.

Q2 Jake is a keen gardener, if there's a plant that he's particularly pleased with he usually takes a **cutting** (rather than growing new plants from the **seeds**). Suggest a reason why.

....

....

Seeds are produced by sexual reproduction.

Q3 **Identical twins** are natural **clones**.

a) Explain how the way they are formed makes identical twins **genetically identical**.

....

b) If identical twins are genetically identical, what factors must be responsible for any differences between them?

....

Q4 A scientist was studying a population of plants in an area. She looked at a **mature** plant and four younger ones that surrounded it. She wanted to know if the young plants had been produced by **sexual** or **asexual** reproduction. She recorded the **characteristics** of the five plants.

Plant	Flower Colour	Leaf Colour	Seed Colour	Seed Shape
A (mature plant)	White	Green	Green	Round
B	White	Green	Green	Wrinkled
C	White	Green	Green	Round
D	Pink	Green	Brown	Wrinkled
E	White	Green and yellow	Green	Wrinkled

Which plant(s) could have been formed by **asexual** reproduction from **plant A**? Explain your answer.

....

....

Module B1 — You and Your Genes

Genetic Disorders

Q1 The family tree below shows a family with a history of **cystic fibrosis**. Both Libby and Anne are pregnant. They know the sexes of their babies but not whether they have the disorder.

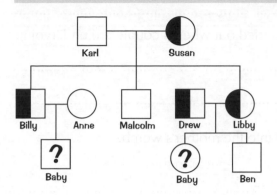

Karl   Susan
Billy   Anne   Malcolm   Drew   Libby
? Baby   **?** Baby   Ben

Key
☐ Male
◯ Female
◨ ◖ Carrier
■ ● Sufferer

a) It is possible to have the allele for cystic fibrosis, yet not know it because you show no symptoms. How is this possible?

....

....

....

....

b) Complete the table to show the percentage chances of Libby's and Annes's babies being carriers and sufferers.

	Carrier	Sufferer
Libby		
Anne		

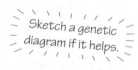
Sketch a genetic diagram if it helps.

Q2 **Huntington's disorder** is caused by a **dominant** allele.

a) It is possible for a person to pass the disorder on to their children unknowingly. Why is this?

....

....

b) What symptoms might someone suffering from Huntington's disorder display?

....

Q3 The table compares the **survival rates** of those born in 1960 and 1980 suffering from **disorder X**. Use this data to complete the passage below by circling the correct word(s).

Year of birth	Percentage of sufferers surviving to the age of:					
	5	10	15	20	25	30
1960	72	58	47	39	31	24
1980	89	85	79	74	69	

People with disorder X are **living longer** / **dying younger** as time goes on.

Of those born in **1960** / **1980** half had died before the age of 15. About

half / **twice** / **three times** as many people born in 1980 survived to the age

of 25 than those born in 1960. The data **indicates** / **does not indicate** that

people are living longer because of improvements in health care.

Genetic Testing

Q1   Rod and Jane are currently undergoing **IVF treatment**.

a)   What do the letters IVF stand for? ....

b)   Give two reasons why **genetic screening** may be carried out when a couple are undergoing IVF.

....

....

c)   The embryos are screened before being implanted into the mother's womb.
    What name is given to this process?

....

d)   Approximately 1 in every 2500 babies born in the UK will have cystic fibrosis.   About 600 000
    babies are born in the UK each year. How many would you expect to have cystic fibrosis?

....

Q2   Give one **objection** people have to the genetic testing of **fetuses**.

....

....

Q3   Give an example of how genetic testing could lead to **discrimination**.

....

....

Q4   **Children** and **adults** can be genetically tested to give an **indication** of their risk of getting a disease
    later in life. Two diseases that can be tested for are **colorectal cancer** and **ovarian cancer**.
    Use the information about the two diseases to say if the statements below are true or false.

- Genetic testing for colorectal cancer identifies people with a high risk of getting the disease.
  These people can then have regular screening for the cancer, which considerably increases their
  chances of survival.

- Less than half the women identified by genetic testing, as at risk of ovarian cancer actually go
  on to develop the disease. There is no effective screening for ovarian cancer and the only thing
  that can be done to remove the risk is to have the ovaries removed.

	True	False
a) The test for ovarian cancer is not very reliable.	☐	☐
b) Testing for a high risk of getting colorectal cancer is more useful than testing for the risk of ovarian cancer because there is no effective screening method for ovarian cancer.	☐	☐
c) The only way to remove the risk of ovarian cancer is to remove the ovaries.	☐	☐

Gene Therapy and Ethics

Q1 Tick the boxes to show whether the following statements about gene therapy are **true** or **false**.

	True	False

a) It can only be carried out on unborn babies.

b) It is readily available for a wide range of disorders.

c) It is 100% reliable.

d) It works by inserting a healthy copy of a gene.

Q2 One possible use of gene therapy is the treatment of **cystic fibrosis**.

a) What **symptoms** would someone suffering from cystic fibrosis display?

....

b) Describe how gene therapy could be used to treat sufferers of cystic fibrosis.

....

....

c) Describe a **problem** associated with the treatment.

....

Q3 Some people **inherit** faulty versions of genes that make them more likely to suffer from **breast cancer**.

a) Describe how could gene therapy could be used to help these people?

....

....

b) Why can't this be done at the moment?

....

c) Why would it be possible for someone who had this treatment to still get breast cancer?

....

Q4 While gene therapy has the potential to improve lives, some people fear that it could be **dangerous**. Describe a concern that people have.

....

....

....

Stem Cells

Q1   Tick the boxes to show whether the following statements are **true** or **false**.

	True	False
a) Most cells in your body are specialised to carry out a specific role.	☐	☐
b) Stem cells can be found in early embryos.	☐	☐
c) Cells of multicellular organisms become specialised during early development of the organism.	☐	☐

Q2   **Embryonic stem cells** have not gone through the process of **differentiation**.

a)   What is meant by the term differentiation?

....

b)   Suggest how embryonic stem cell research could lead to a cure for **diabetes**.

....

....

c)   **Adult stem cells** are already used in the treatment of some diseases.

   i)   Describe how they are used to treat sickle cell anaemia.

   ....

   ....

   ii)   Why are embryonic stem cells of **greater interest** to scientists than adult stem cells?

   ....

d)   How might a scientist culture one specific type of cell?

....

Q3   Many people **disagree** about the use of stem cells.

a)   Give two arguments in favour of the use of stem cells.

....

....

b)   Give two arguments against the use of stem cells.

....

....

Top Tips: Stem cells are a bit of a controversial issue. If a question pops up on the exam you must give a balanced answer, even if you have really, really strong views about their use.

Science and Ethics

Q1 Read the passage and answer the questions that follow.

Genetic testing of unborn babies reaches an all time high

Genetic testing can be carried out during IVF and only embryos without the faulty allele are implanted into the mother's womb. Fetuses in the mother's womb can also be tested giving parents the option to terminate the pregnancy.

Scientists have found the faulty version of the gene that causes disorder Z (a degenerative nervous system disorder) and have been quick to develop a test for it. The test has been offered since 2000. The graph on the right shows the number babies born with disease Z in country A since the test was introduced.

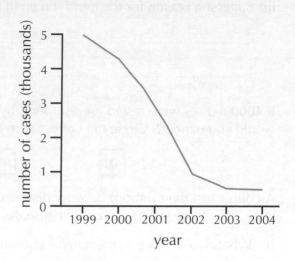

Genetic testing is not without its risks. One method of testing unborn babies is called amniocentesis — fluid from around the fetus (containing fetal cells) is extracted with a syringe and tested. If amniocentesis is carried out there is about a 1% chance of miscarriage.

Some people are against any kind of genetic testing. They think it implies that people with a genetic disorder are inferior to the 'genetically healthy'. Issues are also raised about what action to take if the result of the test is positive. Should the fetus be terminated? — Some people think that they shouldn't because they have a right to life. Other people think that they should as they might suffer their whole lives and might be a burden to their family.

Some people also think that genetic testing for diseases is a 'slippery slope' towards selecting for non-health related characteristics, e.g. eye colour. It may be possible in the future to test for the intelligence of babies before they are born. However, there are a lot of genes involved in the inheritance of intelligence and the environment has a big part to play in determining it. At the moment scientists can only test for single genes.

Science and Ethics

a) For country A:

   i) How many babies were born with disorder Z the **year before** the test was introduced?

     ....

   ii) Describe the **trend** shown in the graph.

     ....

   iii) Suggest a **reason** for the trend shown in the graph.

     ....

     ....

b) If **4000** fetuses were tested for disorder Z by **amniocentesis** how many **miscarriages** would you expect? Circle the correct answer.

                        4   **40**   **400**

c) A couple test their unborn baby for disorder Z and it is found to carry the faulty version of the gene, which means it will have the disease.

   i) What two things can the parents choose to do?

     1. ....

     2. ....

   ii) The couple already have **two** children that **suffer** from disorder Z.
How do you think this might affect their choice about what action to take?

     ....

     ....

d) The article asks, "Should the fetus be terminated".
Is this a question that can be addressed using a **scientific approach**? Explain your answer.

     ....

     ....

e) **i)** Is it possible to test an unborn baby's genes to determine its **intelligence**?

     ....

   ii) Should scientists test an unborn baby's genes to determine its intelligence?
Explain your answer.

     ....

     ....

Chemicals From The Earth

Q1 Complete the following passage by choosing from the words below using each word only once.

nitrogen   oxygen   composition   carbon   1%

constant   concentrations   water vapour   aluminium   variable

Data collected from various parts of the world has shown that the

.... of nitrogen, oxygen and argon in the atmosphere are

pretty much .... The current .... of the

atmosphere is 78% ...., 21% .... and

.... argon. There are small quantities of other gases such

as .... dioxide and ....

Q2 Daniel is investigating the **air quality** in his home town.

a) Daniel took four air samples in the town centre at 12 o'clock. He analysed each one for carbon dioxide, his results are shown below. Which do you think is anomalous? Circle the correct answer.

A 381 ppm   **B 380** ppm   **C 365**ppm   **D 380**ppm

b) Suggest a reason why the anomalous result might have been obtained.

....

c) Explain why Daniel took several samples rather than just one.

....

....

Q3 a) Tick the boxes to show whether the following statements are **true** or **false**.

	True	False
i) Most of the fuels we burn in cars are carbohydrates.	☐	☐
ii) Hydrocarbons contain only carbon and hydrogen atoms.	☐	☐
iii) Diesel fuel is a compound of hydrocarbons.	☐	☐

b) Write a corrected version for the two false statements.

....

....

Chemicals From The Earth

Q4 The majority of fuels we burn are **hydrocarbons**.

a) Where do we get hydrocarbons from?

....

b) Draw a diagram to show the structure of the hydrocarbon pentane.

c) Give one difference between the hydrocarbons found in **petrol** and those found in **diesel**.

....

Q5 Most liquid fuels are a **mixture** of hydrocarbons. The data below shows how the **boiling points** of hydrocarbons vary with the number of carbon atoms in the molecule.

Number of carbon atoms	Boiling point /°C
5	36
6	69
7	98
8	126
10	174
11	196
12	216

a) Plot a scatter graph of this data and draw a line of best fit. _Don't forget to label the axes._

b) Using your graph, predict the boiling point of the hydrocarbon with **nine** carbon atoms.

....

c) Describe the correlation between the number of carbon atoms and the boiling point of the hydrocarbon.

....

....

Chemical Reactions: Combustion

Q1   Tick the boxes to show whether there are the correct number of atoms on either side of these equations.

	correct	incorrect

a)  $Cu\,O + H \rightarrow Cu + H\,O\,H$ ☐ ☐

b)  $Na\,O\,H + H\,Cl \rightarrow Na\,Cl + H\,O\,H$ ☐ ☐

c) $C\,C + O\,O \rightarrow C\,O \quad C\,O$ ☐ ☐

d) $N + H\,H \rightarrow H\,N\,H$ with H on top   ☐ ☐

e) $2Na + 2H_2O \rightarrow NaOH + H_2$ ☐ ☐

f) $CH_4 + 2O_2 \rightarrow 2H_2O + CO_2$ ☐ ☐

g) $HCl + CuO \rightarrow CuCl_2 + H_2O$ ☐ ☐

Q2   Hydrocarbons are **compounds** of **hydrogen** and **carbon** only.

a)   Complete the diagram below to show what happens when the hydrocarbon methane is burnt in plenty of oxygen.

$H\,C\,H$ (with H around C) $+$ $O\,O$ / $O\,O$ $\rightarrow$

b)   What name is given to this type of reaction? ....

c)   Describe what happens, in this reaction, to:

i)   the hydrogen atoms in the fuel. ....

....

ii)   the carbon atoms in the fuel. ....

....

d)   How are the products of combustion different when **carbon** is burnt rather than methane?

....

<u>*Top Tips:*</u>   The letters in a symbol equation represent the atoms and the numbers show how many of each 'thing' there are. For example, in $2H_2O$, the big 2 means that there are two molecules of H_2O and the little 2 means that there are two atoms of hydrogen in each H_2O molecule.

Fuels and Pollutants

Q1 Complete the following passage using the words below.

| products | solid | irritant | destroyed | chemical | asthma | properties | gas |

When a .... reaction takes place, no atoms are ....

and none are made. This is known as conservation of atoms. The ....

of a reaction can have very different .... to those of the reactants.

For example, sulfur (a yellow ....) reacts with oxygen (a colourless

...............................) to form sulfur dioxide — a colourless gas that's an

.... and can trigger .... attacks.

Q2 Ernest put some hot **sodium** into a gas jar containing **chlorine**. The sodium burst into flames and a **white solid** was formed.

a) Complete the diagram to show the reaction that took place. Label the reactants and products.

(Na) (Na) + (Cl)(Cl) →

b) What is the chemical name of the product?

....

c) Do you think the properties of the products will be different from those of the reactants? Explain your answer.

....

....

d) Describe how the diagram you have drawn shows conservation of atoms.

....

....

Q3 Give an example of how **pollutants** can **harm humans** directly and indirectly.

a) Directly ....

b) Indirectly ....

Pollution: Carbon

Q1 Different forms of **carbon pollution** cause different problems.
For each of the following give an example of a **problem** caused.

a) Carbon dioxide. ....

....

b) Carbon monoxide. ....

....

c) Particulate carbon. ....

....

Q2 The graph shows how the **carbon monoxide** concentrations
in the air changed during a typical Monday in a large city.

a) On Monday mornings between 06:00 and 09:00 the **traffic** is increasingly heavy.

i) Is there a correlation between carbon monoxide concentration and the level of traffic?
Explain your answer.

....

....

ii) Do you think that an increase in one factor causes an increase in the other?
Explain your answer.

....

....

b) Would this data set convince the scientific community of a link between traffic levels and carbon
monoxide concentration? Explain your answer.

....

....

c) Why is carbon monoxide produced when hydrocarbon fuel burns in a car engine?

....

Pollution: Carbon

Q3 **Carbon dioxide** can be removed from the atmosphere **naturally**.

a) Which process do green plants use to remove carbon dioxide from the atmosphere?

....

b) Explain why the world's **oceans** can affect atmospheric carbon dioxide levels.

....

Q4 Scientists at the Mauna Loa observatory in Hawaii have been measuring **atmospheric CO$_2$** levels for over **60 years**. The table shows the yearly average levels of carbon dioxide in the atmosphere from 1968 to 2000.

Year	CO$_2$ concentration / ppm
1968	322
1972	327
1976	332
1980	338
1984	344
1988	351
1992	355
1996	362
2000	368

Don't forget to label the axes.

a) Plot a line graph of the data.

b) Using your graph, estimate the concentration of carbon dioxide in 1974.

....

c) i) By how much did the carbon dioxide concentration increase between 1976 and 1996?

....

ii) Express this as a percentage increase.

....

d) All the data in the table has been shown to be **reliable**. What does this mean?

....

....

....

Pollution: Sulfur

Q1 Complete the following passage using the words below

> Coal is a **carbon** / **hydrocarbon** based fuel. Coal burnt in power stations often
> contains impurities — the impurity that causes the biggest problems is **silicon** / **sulfur**.
> When coal undergoes combustion this impurity reacts with **carbon dioxide** / **oxygen**
> in the air to give **sulfur dioxide** / **silicon oxide**.

Q2 Name the **compounds** described below.

a) A compound that contains two oxygen atoms joined to one sulfur atom.

....

b) A compound formed when sulfur dioxide reacts with moisture in clouds.

....

Q3 Clare is investigating how the concentration of **atmospheric pollutants** that cause acid rain affect the life span of a **limestone** headstone. She carried out the following experiment.

> 1. Pour 25 cm³ of 0.1 mol/dm³ acid into a conical flask.
> 2. Add 1 g of small limestone chips and time how long it takes for them to completely dissolve.
> 3. Repeat the experiment three times using 0.1 mol/dm³ acid.
> 4. Repeat steps 1 – 3 using more concentrated, 0.2 mol/dm³, acid instead of 0.1 mol/dm³ acid.

mol/dm³ is a unit of concentration

a) Why is it a good idea for a second scientist to carry out the experiment?

....

b) What sort of correlation should Clare expect between the concentration of acid and the time taken for the limestone chips to dissolve?

....

....

c) Give an example of an environmental problem caused by acid rain, other than damage to limestone structures.

....

....

Pollution: Nitrogen

Q1   Tick the boxes to show whether the following statements are **true** or **false**.

		True	False
a)	The atmosphere contains about 87% nitrogen.	☐	☐
b)	Under normal conditions nitrogen in the atmosphere is unreactive.	☐	☐
c)	Nitrogen pollution is formed from impurities in fuels.	☐	☐
d)	Nitrogen dioxide combines with oxygen and water to form sulfuric acid.	☐	☐

Q2   **Nitrogen oxides** are pollutants that can cause **acid rain**.

a)   Complete the diagram to show the two stages in the formation of nitrogen dioxide from nitrogen and oxygen.

b)   Describe the conditions needed for **nitrogen monoxide** to form, and give an example of where this reaction might take place.

....

....

c)   Name the product formed when nitrogen dioxide reacts with moisture in the atmosphere.

....

Q3   A scientist was investigating whether **NO$_x$** is produced during **electrical storms**. He measured the **nitric acid** concentration of the rain water produced during an electrical storm.

a)   What does NO$_x$ stand for?

....

b)   Explain why NO$_x$ might be produced during electrical storms?

....

c)   Would it matter whether the experiment was carried out in central London or in the middle of the Yorkshire moors? Explain your answer.

....

....

d)   Suggest why it will be hard to ensure the experiment is a fair test.

....

....

Pollution: Nitrogen

Q4 The table below shows some data about the complete combustion of three household **fuels** — coal, oil and natural gas.

Fuel	Energy output (kJ/g)	Mass of carbon dioxide produced (g)
coal	30	95
oil	48	82
natural gas	86	63

a) Which fuel produces the most energy per gram burned? ....

b) Which fuel makes the greatest contribution to the greenhouse effect? Explain your answer.

....

....

Q5 Mary measured the NO_2 concentration in the middle of a large town at 2pm on a weekday. She used ten gas analysers to sample air from the same area **simultaneously**. Her results are shown below.

Analyser	A	B	C	D	E	F	G	H	I	J
NO_2 (ppb)	21.5	21.6	21.9	22.0	21.7	21.7	21.8	24.6	21.9	21.5

a) Are any of the values anomalous? If so, which?

....

b) Suggest a possible reason for any anomalous results.

....

c) Calculate the best estimate of the true value of the NO_2 concentration.

....

d) How do you think the NO_2 concentration at 6pm the same day would be different, if at all, from the results above? Explain your answer.

....

Top Tips: The problem with atmospheric pollutants is that they generally just hang around, causing problems. And we're constantly adding more of them — which can only make things worse.

Interpreting Pollution Data

Q1   Read the passage below and answer the questions that follow.

Air pollution — getting to the heart of the matter

A team of scientists from the University of Southern California have found that high levels of pollution (caused by traffic and industry) could trigger atherosclerosis — the narrowing of arteries[1]. Narrowing of the arteries is caused by a thickening of the artery lining. This reduces blood flow in the artery.

Links between narrowed arteries and factors like smoking, obesity and diabetes are well established, but this report provides evidence for a link with air pollution. The study involved 798 people over the age of 40 living in the Los Angeles area. The thickness of the lining of their carotid arteries (the main artery in the neck) was measured using ultrasound.

The scientists also recorded pollution levels around the volunteers' homes. They measured the number of pollutant particles with a diameter of 2.5 micrometres or less. These particles, known as $PM_{2.5}$, are commonly produced by burning fossil fuels, e.g. petrol in cars. The levels of $PM_{2.5}$ were found to range from 5.2 to 26.9 micrograms per cubic metre ($\mu g/m^3$).

[1] Nino Künzli, Michael Jerrett, Wendy J. Mack, Bernardo Beckerman, Laurie LaBree, Frank Gilliland, Duncan Thomas, John Peters, and Howard N. Hodis. Ambient Air Pollution and Atherosclerosis in Los Angeles. Environ Health Perspect 113:201–206 (2005).

The study found that the higher the $PM_{2.5}$ level, the thicker the artery lining. On average, the artery lining was 5.9% thicker for every extra 10 $\mu g/m^3$ of $PM_{2.5}$ particles in the air. The results varied with age and sex, with the strongest link being in women over the age of 60, as shown in figure 1.

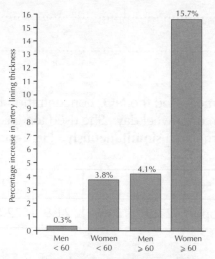

Figure 1. Percentage increase in thickness of artery lining for every 10 $\mu g/m^3$ increase in pollution.

Exactly how air pollution leads to artery narrowing is still unknown. One theory is that air pollution causes the body to produce chemicals that trigger arterial damage. Given that heart disease is now the biggest killer in many developed countries, the findings of this study could have a major influence on government decisions about public health.

Interpreting Pollution Data

a) Atherosclerosis is the build-up of fatty materials in the arteries.

  i) Circle any factors below that have been linked to atherosclerosis.

  measles   smoking   obesity   tallness   hay fever   diabetes

  ii) In which artery did the scientists measure the build-up of fatty materials?

  ....

  iii) How did the scientists measure the thickness of fatty material lining the artery?

  ....

b) The scientists measured the levels of $PM_{2.5}$ particles around the volunteers' homes.

  i) What are $PM_{2.5}$ particles?

  ....

  ....

  ii) Describe one cause of $PM_{2.5}$ pollution.

  ....

  iii) What was the lowest concentration of $PM_{2.5}$ found in the study?

  ....

  iv) According to the article, how might $PM_{2.5}$ pollution lead to arterial damage?

  ....

  ....

c) When large-scale health studies are carried out, it's usually important to include data from many different countries. Tick the box next to the most likely explanation for this.

  Scientists like to travel to different parts of the world. ☐

  To ensure the conclusion is valid all over the world. ☐

  To make people in other countries feel included. ☐

Top Tips: Questions like this might seem a bit scary but the key is not to panic. You get the article before the exam so it should be familiar, and you'll be able to answer all the questions using the information in the article or what you've learnt from the rest of the specification.

Interpreting Pollution Data

d) Tick the box next to the statement which best describes what the study shows.

People living in areas of high pollution all suffer from atherosclerosis. ☐

Only people over the age of 60 will suffer from atherosclerosis. ☐

The risk of atherosclerosis is higher for people living in high pollution areas. ☐

e) The strongest link between pollution levels and artery narrowing was in women over 60. Women over 60 made up 23.3% of the volunteers.

i) How many of the volunteers were women over 60?

....

ii) A 62 year old woman living in an area of Los Angeles with a $PM_{2.5}$ pollution level of 8.0 µg/m³ had an artery lining thickness of 100 µm. Estimate the likely artery lining thickness of a 62 year old woman living in an area of Los Angeles with a $PM_{2.5}$ pollution level of 13 µg/m³.

mine's bigger than yours

....

....

....

iii) A 42 year old male had an artery lining thickness 100 µm. He lived in an area of Los Angeles with a $PM_{2.5}$ concentration of 10 µg/m³. Another 42 year old male had the thickness of his carotid artery lining measured as 104 µm. Estimate the $PM_{2.5}$ concentration in the area where the second man lives.

....

f) Some scientists feel that further large-scale studies are needed to assess the health impacts of long-term exposure to air pollution.

i) Suggest why extra data would be helpful.

....

....

....

ii) From the study described in the article, is it possible to say that 'air pollution causes atherosclerosis'? Explain your answer.

....

....

....

Reducing Pollution

Q1   Cars are a major source of **pollution**, though technological advances could help to **reduce** this.

a)   Petrol stations now sell low-sulfur fuel. How could this help to reduce pollution?

....

b)   Catalytic converters change nitrogen monoxide into which two gases?

....

c)   What is the benefit of a catalytic converter changing carbon monoxide into carbon dioxide?

....

d)   Suggest why it often takes a long time for pollution-reducing technologies such as catalytic converters to become widely used.

....

Q2   The best way to **reduce** CO_2 pollution is to **reduce** the amount of fossil fuels we burn.

a)   One way reductions could be made is if everyone used public transport instead of cars. Suggest why this is unlikely to happen.

....

....

b)   How do power stations that burn natural gas reduce sulfur dioxide pollution?

....

Q3   **Exhaust emission** checks are an important part of the **MOT test**. The test centres use a meter to check for **carbon monoxide** and **hydrocarbons**. George's car is three years old and had the following test results:

	George's car	Maximum level of emissions allowed		
		1st August 1992 - present	1st August 1986 - 31st July 1992	Before 1st August 1986
Carbon monoxide level	0.2%	0.3%	3.5%	4.5%
Hydrocarbon level	4 ppm	200 ppm	1200 ppm	1200 ppm

a)   Did George's car pass the emissions test?

....

b)   Based on the levels of emissions allowed in the past, would you say that the car was more efficient than a typical car made in 1991? Explain your answer.

....

....

Sustainable Development

Q1   Read the following passage and answer the questions that follow.

Fuel Cells — the future of sustainability?

A fuel cell is an electrochemical device that combines hydrogen and oxygen to generate electricity. Fuel cells can be produced on any scale to give the desired power output. They have a wide range of applications — the one that interests most people is replacement of the standard car engine. Cars powered by fuel cells are basically electric cars that don't rely on batteries — they generate their own electricity.

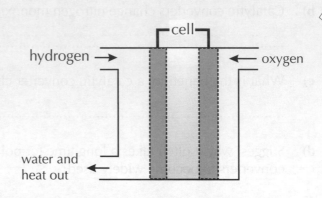

Fuel cells have the potential to reduce pollution.

With the potential to replace traditional petrol and diesel engines, fuel cells have a number of advantages:
- They produce no greenhouse gases (such as carbon dioxide), particulates or nitrogen oxide emissions. In fact the only product is water.
- Cars powered by fuel cells only use energy when they're moving, unlike a traditional car which uses fuel when stationary. Vehicles powered by a hydrogen fuel cell can be three times more efficient than those powered by petrol.
- They're very quiet compared to normal vehicle engines.

One big disadvantage is refuelling. Currently, cars powered by fuel cells can only cover a short distance before they need refuelling. However, a spokesperson for one of the large car manufacturers said that by 2010, they will have designed a fuel cell car that can go as far on a full tank as a petrol car, "without the fuel tank being twice the size of the car."

The key to making fuel cells sustainable lies with the production of the hydrogen fuel. Producing hydrogen needs a lot of energy, and this has to come from renewable energy resources such as solar, wind or biomass — or else it's still causing a lot of environmental damage.

Many fuel cell powered cars are still in early stages of development so it'll be a while before we see whether they make it to mass production.

Many see the hydrogen fuel cell as crucial in a sustainable future. It can not only reduce our dependence on oil, but will also benefit the environment by reducing emissions of greenhouse gases and pollutants that affect our air quality.

Sustainable Development

a) Fuel cells generate electrical energy from hydrogen and oxygen.

    i) Give two types of pollution that fuel cells have the potential to reduce.

    ....

    ii) What is the only product from a fuel cell?

    ....

b) The article says that the use of fuel cells would reduce our dependence on oil.
What do we currently depend on oil for?

....

....

c) Give one way in which the standard car engine has contributed to environmental problems.

....

....

d) In the article, the spokesperson for the car manufacturer jokes about the size
of the fuel tank needed in a car powered by a fuel cell. Suggest why a fuel
tank for hydrogen would have to be a lot bigger than a fuel tank for petrol.

....

e) The fuel cell is seen by many as "crucial in a sustainable future".

    i) What is meant by the term 'sustainable development'?

    ....

    ....

    ii) Hydrogen fuel cells can produce energy for cars and a range of other applications.
How could this help our society to develop sustainably?

    ....

    ....

    ....

    iii) Some people argue that fuel cells are not a sustainable technology because
energy is needed to produce the hydrogen, and this energy normally comes from
burning fossil fuels. How does the article suggest this problem can be overcome?

    ....

    ....

The Changing Earth

Q1 Here are some jumbled up sentences about the rock cycle. Number the statements 1 – 6 to put them in the right order. The first one is done for you.

[ ] Sedimentary rocks can either be lifted back to the Earth's surface or sink deeper to form new types of rock.

[1] Rocks on the Earth's surface are constantly being eroded.

[ ] Over a long time, many layers of sediment build up.

[ ] Eventually, the rock returns the surface and the cycle repeats.

[ ] Rock particles (called sediment) are gradually transported to the bottom of the sea.

[ ] These layers are squashed together to form sedimentary rocks.

Q2 Tick the boxes to show whether each of the following statements are true or false. **True False**

a) If rocks weren't continually recycled to make new mountains, all land would be at sea level. [ ] [ ]

b) Mount Everest is continually being worn away by erosion. [ ] [ ]

c) Folds in rocks suggest that huge temperatures and pressures have moved the rock in the past. [ ] [ ]

d) Although rocks have moved around in the past, this is no longer happening today. [ ] [ ]

Q3 Scientists have measured the age of some of Earth's rocks using radioactive dating. They have found that the oldest rocks are around **4 billion years old**. Which of these statements can be deduced from **this evidence alone**? Circle the letter(s) next to the correct answer(s).

A The Universe is 4 billion years old.

B All rocks were formed 4 billion years ago.

C The Earth is at least 4 billion years old.

D The Solar System is at least 4 billion years old.

E The rock cycle has been happening for at least 4 billion years.

Be careful — don't assume anything.

Q4 **Volcanoes** play an important part in shaping the surface of the Earth.

a) Explain the role of volcanoes in the rock cycle.

....

b) You can often find fossils in sedimentary rock. Explain why you wouldn't find fossils in the rock formed by volcanoes.

....

....

Observations and Explanations

Q1 Fossils of the **same species** of animal have been found on both sides of the **Atlantic Ocean**. Scientists have put forward two explanations for why fossils of the same species of animal are found in these two very different places.

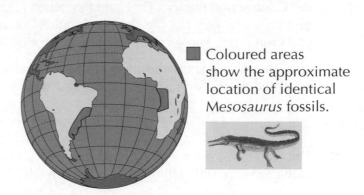

Coloured areas show the approximate location of identical *Mesosaurus* fossils.

a) One explanation is that there used to be '**land bridges**' between the continents — narrow pieces of land that sank into the sea as the Earth cooled. How could the existence of land bridges account for the fossil evidence described above?

....

b) Briefly describe the alternative explanation put forward by Wegener.

....

....

c) Give one other piece of evidence from the diagram that adds weight to the Wegener's explanation.

....

....

Q2 There are many ways for scientists to gather data about the movement of the Earth, e.g. satellites can accurately measure the speeds of various points on the Earth's surface. Decide whether each of the following statements describes **data** or is part of a possible **explanation** of the data.

		Data	Explanation
a)	Parts of the Earth's surface are moving relative to each other.	☐	☐
b)	This 'plate movement' is driven by convection currents in the mantle.	☐	☐
c)	In the past, there was only one large landmass called Pangaea.	☐	☐
d)	The coastlines of continents seem to fit together like a big jigsaw.	☐	☐
e)	Underwater mountains either side of the mid-Atlantic ridge are symmetrical.	☐	☐
f)	The magnetic orientations of rock bands on either side of the mid-Atlantic ridge are also symmetrical.	☐	☐

Observations and Explanations

Q3   In the past, scientists explained the formation of mountains using the **Contraction theory**. They said that when Earth's crust was formed it was very hot. As the crust cooled down it contracted and crumpled. These crumples formed the mountains.

You don't need to know anything else about Contraction theory to answer this question.

a)   Even though we know this theory to be wrong today, it was the accepted theory for many years. Suggest why.

....

b)   The Himalayas are a very high mountain chain in Asia. Scientists have discovered that the Himalayas are still getting higher. Explain why this evidence suggests Contraction theory is wrong.

....

....

c)   Why have scientists only recently been able to measure the height of the Himalayas accurately and precisely enough to tell that they are getter higher?

....

Q4   Wegener put forward his theory of continental drift in 1912. However, it wasn't accepted by the scientific community until about 60 years after its publication.

a)   Give one **scientific** reason why the scientific community found it hard to accept that land masses had actually moved apart.

....

b)   What was it about **Wegener himself** that meant geologists had a hard time accepting his ideas?

....

c)   Why did the discovery that the sea floor is moving apart lead to most scientists accepting the theory?

....

Q5   However convincing the evidence in favour of a scientific theory, we can never **prove** the theory right. But only **one** piece of valid evidence can prove it **wrong**. Why is this?

....

....

> **_Top Tips:_**   Science is all about observations and explanations — a scientist sees something happen that isn't predicted by a current theory, so tries to explain why it happens like that. It can be tough to think up new explanations — then you've got to convince everyone else your theory's right.

The Structure of the Earth

Q1   **Label** this diagram of the Earth's interior and write a **brief description** next to each label.

....

....

....

....

....

....

Q2   Choose from the words in this list to complete the paragraph below.

solid   heat   tectonic   mantle   convection   crust   radioactive   core

.... decay in the .... produces a

lot of .... , which causes the ....

to flow in .... currents. These currents drive the

movement of the Earth's .... plates .

Q3   The table shows the dates on which a particular city was hit by earthquakes.

Date	Magnitude (severity of quake)
12th Dec 1632	6.9
14th Jul 1721	7.2
23rd May 1810	3.8
12th Jan 1812	3.2
12th Aug 1904	8.6
14th Feb 1990	7.4

a)   When did the largest earthquake happen?

....

b)   Suggest why the 1812 earthquake was unexpected.

....

....

c)   Based on the data, for what year would you predict the next earthquake? ....

d)   Why is it difficult to predict when an earthquake is going to happen?

....

Q4   Using the idea of tectonics, explain why **mountains** usually occur in **chains**, rather than singularly.

....

....

The Solar System

Q1 Here are some questions about how objects in the night sky appear to the naked eye.

a) Some planets look like stars in the night sky. What is different about the light we see from them?

....

b) Why do we only see comets for a very short part of their orbit?

....

....

Q2 Write down these Solar System objects in order of **increasing size**.

planet   moon   Sun   comet

....

Q3 Choose words from the list to fill in the gaps in the following passage.

objects   star   expanded   Earth   contracted   dust   hot   Sun

The Solar System started as a cloud of .... and gas. Over millions of

years, this cloud .... under the force of gravity. At its centre, the cloud

became .... enough and dense enough to form a

.... (the ....). Other parts of the cloud gradually

clumped together to become the other .... in the Solar System.

Q4 Scientists study **meteorites** found in Antarctica to find out about the early Solar System.

a) What is a meteorite? ....

b) What method do scientists use to find out how old these meteorites are?

Scientists use the same method to date igneous rocks on Earth.

....

c) To the nearest billion years, what is our current estimate of the age of the Solar System?

....

Danger from Space

Q1 Here is a list of statements about potential **dangers** from space.
Tick the correct boxes to show whether each statement is true or false.

True False

a) Every day, dust and tiny rocks from space enter the Earth's atmosphere. ☐ ☐

b) The Earth has been involved in collisions with very large objects from space in the past. ☐ ☐

c) Small objects from space often burn up harmlessly in the Earth's atmosphere. ☐ ☐

d) There are fewer craters on the Earth than the Moon because there have been fewer collisions. ☐ ☐

Q2 Choose words from the list to fill in the gaps in the following passage.

extinct   tsunamis   large   fires   small   dust
climate   ocean   fast   sunlight

If a .... asteroid collided with the Earth, it could

cause a huge amount of damage. .... could be

formed if the asteroid landed in an .... On land

there could be ...., and lots of hot rocks and

.... would be thrown up into the atmosphere.

This could change the .... by blocking out

....

Q3 Bob the astronomer is monitoring the path of a nearby asteroid. He calculates that there is a **1 in 50** chance of the asteroid colliding with the Earth in the next ten years.

a) How do astronomers monitor the paths of asteroids?

....

b) What is the chance of the asteroid **not** hitting the Earth in the next ten years?

....

c) Some asteroids with this chance of hitting the Earth would be of no concern. However other asteroids might cause world-wide panic. Explain why.

....

....

Module P1 — The Earth in the Universe

Danger from Space

Q4   An asteroid impact has been blamed for the **mass extinction** about 65 million years ago.

a)   What is meant by a mass extinction?

....

b)   Explain how the fossil record provides evidence that dinosaurs became extinct 65 million years ago.

....

c)   Iridium is an element commonly found in asteroids but not in the Earth's crust. Explain how the discovery of iridium in sedimentary rocks from 65 million years ago has added weight to the theory that the dinosaurs were made extinct due to an asteroid collision.

....

....

Q5   The table below shows the data, as we went to press, that NASA has collected about asteroids that might collide with the Earth.

Asteroid	Chance of collision with Earth (per million in next 100 years)	Estimated diameter (km)
2006 SF281	2.3	0.020
2006 UO	0.1	0.210
2006 SC	33	0.032
2006 QV89	320	0.030
2006 UD17	0.013	0.740

Courtesy NASA/JPL-Caltech

a)   Not all the asteroids above would do the same amount of damage if they collided with us.

   i)   Which asteroid would be likely to do the most damage if it collided with the Earth?

   ....

   ii)   Calculate the risk of this asteroid colliding with the Earth in the next 100 years as a percentage.

   ....

b)   **i)**   Which asteroid has the highest risk of a collision? ....

   ii)   Why is this unlikely to be a problem for us on Earth?

   ....

Top Tips: If you read 'Danger from Space' and thought **aagghh** alien invasion, then don't worry — this page is just about giant rocks hitting the Earth and causing mass extinctions. If meteors do worry you, just remember this — space is a big place, so the chance of anything hitting Earth is tiny.

Beyond the Solar System

Q1 Fill in the blanks in the sentences below using some of the words from the list.

Milky Way   Sun   billions   galaxies   110   big   planet   stars   Universe   billion   millions

   a) The Sun is about .... times bigger than the Earth. The diameter of the Milky Way is about 600 .... times the diameter of the Sun.

   b) The distance between .... is usually millions of times more than the distance between ....

Q2 The **light-year** is a unit of distance.

   a) If the speed of light in a vacuum is 3.0×10^8 m/s, show that 1 light-year is approximately equal to 9.5×10^{15} m.

Start by working out the number of seconds in a year.

....

....

   b) The most distant objects that the Hubble Space telescope has seen are about 12 billion light-years away. How many metres are there in 12 billion light-years?

....

   c) A nearby star, Sirius, is 8.2×10^{16} m away.

     i) Approximately how many light-years away is it? ....

     ii) If Sirius suddenly exploded, how long would it be before we could know? ....

Q3 Complete this table using the numbers given below.

Object	Estimated Age	Estimated Diameter
Earth		
Sun		
Milky Way	13.6 billion years	
Universe		

You don't need to know the figures to answer this question.

    5 billion years   5 billion years   13.7 billion years

150 billion light-years   12 800 km   100 000 light-years   1.4 million km

Q4 Many scientists think there might be life elsewhere in the Universe.
Tick the boxes to show whether each of the following statements is true or false.

                                      True   **False**

   a) Scientists have discovered many planets orbiting nearby stars. ☐ ☐

   b) It's more likely that microscopic life exists on alien planets than that intelligent life does. ☐ ☐

   c) There is nothing special about Earth's location that allows it to support life. ☐ ☐

Looking into Space

Q1 Some stars look **brighter** than others in the night sky.

a) Write down two factors that affect how bright a star looks to us from Earth?

1. ....

2. ....

b) When observing the light from stars, astronomers often complain of light pollution. What is light pollution and why is it a problem?

....

....

Q2 The diagram shows two photographs of the same part of the night sky. The photographs were taken 6 months apart.

a) Two of the stars (labelled A and B) appear to have moved, while the rest have stayed in the same places. What does this tell us about stars A and B, and why?

5th January   5th July

....

....

b) Which of the two stars is closer to Earth — star A or star B? Give a reason for your answer.

....

c) Astronomers can use stars' apparent movement (parallax) to calculate the distance to nearby stars fairly accurately. There is more uncertainty in the measurement of distances to very distant stars. Explain why.

....

Q3 When we look into space, we see things as they were in the past.

a) Explain why we are seeing stars as they were in the past.

....

b) SETI is an organisation that searches for extraterrestrial intelligence by looking for **radio signals** transmitted from other planets. Explain why aliens living **200 light-years** away would be unable to detect **us** yet using the same technique.

....

....

The world's first radio station began broadcasting in 1897.

The Life Cycle of Stars

Q1   The Sun will pass through several stages in its life. Write these four stages in the right order.

stable phase   white dwarf   red giant   protostar

....

Q2   Fill in the gaps in this paragraph about the formation of the Sun, using the words below.

contracted   dust   gas   temperature   hydrogen   fusion

helium   gravity   heat   light

The Sun formed from a cloud of .... and ....

This cloud .... under the force of ...., which

made the centre of the cloud .... up. Eventually the

.... was high enough for .... reactions to

take place. In these reactions, nuclei of .... join together to form

.... These reactions give out massive amounts of

.... and heat. This process is still happening today.

Q3   Scientists have discovered over 100 elements that make up everything in the Universe.

a)   How were the elements heavier than helium made?

....

b)   What does this suggest about where the elements that make up the
Earth and everything on it have come from?

....

Q4   The life cycle of a star can take billions of years.

Astronomers discovered the different states in the life cycles of stars by studying many stars.
Would this have been possible if there was only one star in the sky? Explain your answer.

....

....

....

The Life of the Universe

Q1 Here are some statements about the expansion of the Universe. Tick the boxes to show whether each statement describes **data** or is part of an **explanation**.

Data Explanation

a) Most galaxies are moving away from us. ☐ ☐

b) The further away a galaxy is, the faster it is moving away. ☐ ☐

c) The Universe is expanding. ☐ ☐

d) The Universe started from a single point. ☐ ☐

Q2 Many cosmologists believe that the Universe began with a Big Bang.

a) Briefly describe the Big Bang theory.

....

....

b) How many years ago do cosmologists think the Big Bang happened?

....

c) According to Big Bang theory, what is happening to space itself?

....

Q3 The **eventual fate** of the Universe depends on its current rate of expansion, and how quickly the expansion is slowing down.

a) Which of these quantities determines how quickly the expansion of the Universe is slowing down? Circle the correct answer.

Friction in the Universe   Mass of the Universe

Temperature of the Universe

b) Explain why this quantity is very difficult to measure.

....

....

c) Describe two possible fates of the Universe.

1. ....

2. ....

The Life of the Universe

Q4 The graph shows the distances from Earth and speeds of some galaxies based on modern measurements.

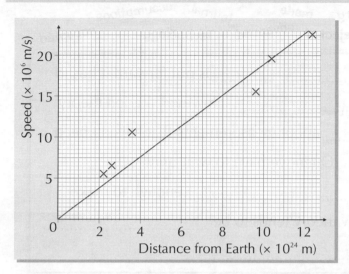

a) Which of these statements can be deduced from the shape of the graph? Circle the letter(s) next to correct answer(s).

A There is a correlation between the speed of galaxies and their distance from Earth.

B The speed is proportional to the distance from Earth.

C More distant galaxies move faster because they are further away.

b) Suggest a reason why the data points are quite scattered.

....

c) Estimate the speed of a galaxy that's 8×10^{24} m away from us.

....

Q5 The diagram shows four pupils taking part in a demonstration. They are standing in a line, spaced at 0.5 m intervals.

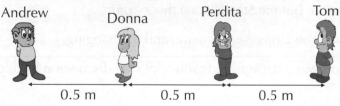

Andrew   Donna   Perdita   Tom

0.5 m   0.5 m   0.5 m

a) The teacher told Andrew to stay still but the others to move so that they were now **one metre** apart from each other. When they did this, the **space** between each pupil doubled. Work out how far:

i) Donna moved ....

ii) Perdita moved ....

iii) Tom moved ....

b) Each pupil took 2 seconds to move. Work out the speed at which Andrew saw each pupil moving away from him.

i) Donna's speed: ....

ii) Perdita's speed: ....

iii) Tom's speed: ....

c) Use this demonstration to help you explain the trend in the data shown in Q4.

....

....

Module P1 — The Earth in the Universe

The Scientific Community

Q1 Fill in the gaps in this paragraph about scientific theories, using the words below.

predictions   evidence   theory   made   journal   assumptions
clever   confirmed   sensible   rejected   advanced   technology   accepted

When a new scientific .... is put forward it has to

explain the current .... However, a good theory

makes .... about measurements that haven't been

.... yet. Often we have to wait until

.... is .... enough to make

these measurements. A new theory tends to be ....

once its predictions are ....

Q2 Number these statements 1–6 to put them in chronological order.

☐ Two rival theories were put forward to explain the evidence — the Big Bang theory and the Steady State theory.

☐ Edwin Hubble discovered that the Universe is expanding.

☐ Most scientists believe the Big Bang theory.

☐ The Big Bang theory predicted leftover background radiation from the initial explosion, but the Steady State theory didn't.

☐ Scientists believed the Universe was static and unchanging.

☐ The 'cosmic microwave background radiation' was discovered by accident.

Q3 Before scientific measurements and explanations are accepted by the scientific community, they are usually published in a peer reviewed journal.

a) What is a peer reviewed journal?

....

b) The peer review process helps to make sure that published data is reliable and valid. Explain what is meant by 'reliable data'.

....

Top Tips: Peer review is all about safety in numbers — if only one scientist believes something, he could just be making it up for a laugh, but if loads of scientists think it's true then there's likely to be something in it. Most scientists now accept the Big Bang theory — but they didn't always.

Module P1 — The Earth in the Universe

Microorganisms and Disease

Q1   Disease in humans can be caused by microorganisms.

a)   Name **four** types of microorganism.

....

b)   Explain the difference between the terms **microorganism** and **pathogen**.

....

....

Q2   Circle the correct words to complete the passage below.

Many bacteria can cause an infection when they resist natural barriers, enter the body and start

to **reproduce** / **die** — this can happen quickly because the conditions in the body are **warm** / **dark**.

When lots of bacteria are present, they start to cause **symptoms** / **growth**. This can be due to

bacteria producing poisons called **antibodies** / **toxins**, which can damage the body's **blood** / **cells**.

Microorganisms can **never** / **sometimes** damage cells directly.

Q3   The human body has **natural barriers** to reduce the
risk of harmful microorganisms entering the body.

a)   Explain how each of the following acts as a natural barrier to microorganisms.

i) Skin ....

....

ii) Sweat ....

....

iii) Tears ....

b)   **Stomach acid** can also help to prevent bacterial infections. Explain how it does this.

....

Q4   An experiment was carried out to investigate the **growth
rate** of a bacterium which causes disease in humans.
The experiment was carried out at 37 °C.

a)   Give a reason why the experiment was carried out at 37 °C.

....

b)   **Symptoms** of the disease appear when the number of bacteria reach
100 000 per cm³. Using the graph, state how long after infection symptoms would start to appear.

....

The Immune System

Q1   What is the role of the immune system?

....

Q2   Some white blood cells can produce **antibodies** to deal with invading microorganisms.

  a)   Can an antibody recognise a wide range of microorganisms? Explain your answer.

....

....

  b)   Describe another way white blood cells can help to defend against microorganisms.

....

Q3 a)   Put the stages in order (1-4) to show how **white blood cells** deal with infection caused by a microorganism.

  ☐   The antibodies attach to the microorganism.

  ☐   White blood cells detect the surface antigens of the invading microorganism.

  ☐   An antibody that can attack the microorganism is produced.

  ☐   The microorganism is killed.

  b)   Outline what would happen if the **same** microorganism was encountered again.

....

....

Q4   Underline the correct description of an **antigen**.   A 'foreign' cell.

A chemical that causes disease.   A molecule found on the surface of a microorganism.   A molecule that destroys bacteria.

Q5   Two friends, Mahmood and Chris had a test to see if they needed to be immunised against tuberculosis (TB). The test measured whether they were **already immune** to TB (i.e. if they had enough antibodies specific to TB in their blood). The results showed that Mahmood had a high level of TB antibodies in his blood but Chris did not. It was recommended that Mahmood did not have the TB vaccination, but that Chris should have it.

  a)   Explain why Chris needed the vaccination and Mahmood did not.

....

  b)   Suggest a reason why Mahmood and Chris had such different levels of antibodies in their blood.

....

Vaccination

Q1 Circle the correct words to complete the passage below.

Illness can be due to microorganisms **dying** / **causing damage** before the immune system can destroy them. If you become infected with a microorganism you have been vaccinated against, you **will** / **won't** have specific antibodies in your blood before the infection.

Q2 Most people who catch **mumps** only suffer mild symptoms and death from the disease is extremely rare. If most people can overcome the disease themselves, why is it considered necessary to vaccinate against it?

....

Q3 Vaccination usually involves injecting the body with a **dead** or **inactive** form of a pathogen.

Why do dead microorganisms cause the body to produce antibodies?

....

Q4 A **vaccination programme** was introduced in a country to stop the spread of **disease A**. Parents were advised to have their children vaccinated at the age of 3. Two years later, a survey was done to see the effects of the vaccination programme. The results obtained are shown below.

> Of the children vaccinated, 11% had developed the disease.
> Of the non-vaccinated children, 40% had developed the disease.
> Of the vaccinated children, 10% suffered side effects.
> In 3 cases, the side effects of the vaccination were very serious.

a) Underline any of the statements below that are **possible** explanations for the fact that the injection worked for some and not others.

The vaccine does not work.

The vaccine did not work in some cases because the children had previously suffered from the disease.

You are not expected to know the facts in questions like this – they're just to test your judgement about scientific issues.

The children who did not get the disease were in better general health.

The vaccine was contaminated.

b) Explain why vaccinations are never considered to be **completely safe**.

....

....

Top Tips: Vaccination is a really effective way of controlling the spread of a disease. There's a small amount of risk involved as the pathogen itself is injected — don't worry side effects are pretty rare.

Vaccination

Q5 Vaccines for some diseases only need to be given to an individual once every 10 years. There is a vaccine available for **influenza** (flu), which is usually given to people that are especially vulnerable, e.g. the elderly. This vaccine needs to be given every year. For some diseases, like **HIV**, there are currently no effective vaccines at all.

a) Why do people have to be vaccinated against flu every year?

....

....

b) Why is it difficult to develop an effective vaccine against HIV?

....

....

Q6 A **course of vaccination** against **disease B** consists of three injections at 5-week intervals, followed by a booster injection 5 years later. The graph shows the average level of antibodies in the patients' blood over the course of the programme.

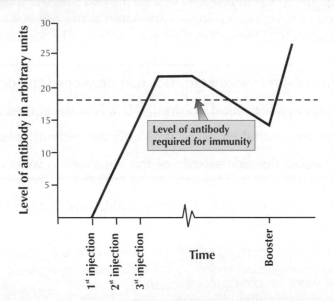

a) Explain why the level of antibodies can be used to measure immunity to a disease.

....

b) Using the graph, explain why:

  i) Three injections are needed initially.

....

  ii) A booster injection is needed after 5 years.

....

Vaccination — Pros and Cons

Q1   Read the passage below and answer the questions that follow.

The MMR Vaccine in the Spotlight

The Government's Health Department is concerned about a possible measles epidemic as parents continue to resist having their children vaccinated against the disease with the MMR vaccine. The graph below shows the number of measles cases in the UK between 1999 and 2004.

The vaccine is given to children when they're 13 months old and protects them against three diseases — measles, mumps and rubella. Mumps can cause meningitis, sterility in men and deafness. Rubella causes little harm unless it's caught in the early stage of pregnancy, when it can cause severe problems in the developing baby. Measles is the most serious of the three diseases, as it can lead to pneumonia, fits, and even death.

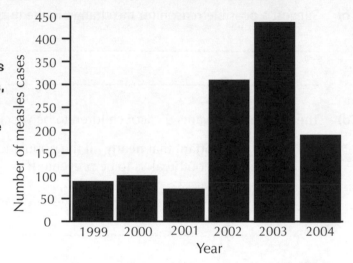

The number of children being vaccinated with the MMR vaccine each year decreased, following a paper published in 1998 which suggested a possible link between the MMR vaccine and the brain condition autism. However, many other studies across the world involving thousands of children have consistently failed to find any link between the vaccination and autism.

The Government's target is for 95% of children to be vaccinated. At present, about 85% are being vaccinated, though this is an increase from a low point of around 80% a few years ago.

Some parents would prefer to have their children vaccinated separately against each disease rather than all at once. This is not recommended by the medical authorities for the following reasons:

1. The separate vaccines have not been tested and licensed in this country.

2. It requires more visits to a surgery and there is a greater likelihood that people will forget.

3. The child has to have three times as many injections.

4. The separate vaccines have been shown to be less effective in provoking an immune response.

The MMR vaccine, like all others, can produce unpleasant side effects in some individuals. Scientists cannot categorically prove that there is no link whatsoever between MMR and autism, as some people demand, but all the evidence suggests that any medical risks of having a child vaccinated with MMR are much less than leaving the child unvaccinated.

Vaccination — Pros and Cons

a) Explain why some parents resist having their children vaccinated with the MMR vaccine.

....

....

b) Circle the disease (that is vaccinated against using MMR) that is thought to be the **most serious**.

Mumps   Measles   Rubella

c) Suggest a possible reason for the change in the number of measles cases **after 2001**.

....

....

d) The government wants 95% of children to be vaccinated.

   i) Why is it important that **nearly all** the population are immunised against
     a disease if an outbreak is to be prevented?

   ....

   ....

   ii) Give an argument **against** forcing 100% of the population to be vaccinated.

   ....

   ....

e) Four reasons are given against the use of separate vaccines for measles, mumps and rubella.
Of these, which one do you think parents would be **most** concerned about.
Give a reason for your answer.

....

....

f) The article states that, "Scientists cannot categorically prove that there is no link whatsoever
between MMR and autism". Explain why this is.

....

....

g) In poorer developing countries there might not be enough money to vaccinate everyone.
Circle the most appropriate way the available vaccines should be used.

To immunise the adults in the country.

In the way that best controls the disease.

Antibiotics

Q1   Explain the difference between an **antibody** and an **antibiotic**.

....

....

Q2   Jenny went to the doctor because she had **flu**. The doctor didn't give her any drugs and advised her to stay in bed for a while. Why wouldn't the doctor give her any antibiotics for her condition?

....

Q3   In 1960, a **new antibiotic** was discovered which was very effective against **disease X**. Doctors have been prescribing this drug ever since. The graph below shows the number of deaths from disease X over a number of years.

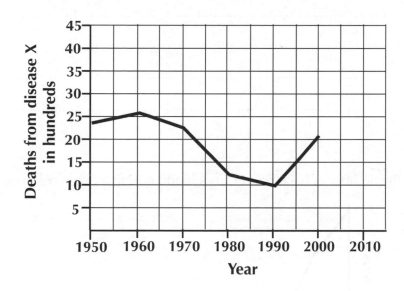

a)   Assuming nothing changes, use the graph to **predict** the number of deaths from disease X in **2010**.

....

b)   Suggest a reason for the **fall** in deaths from the disease between 1960 and 1990.

....

c)   Suggest a reason for the **sudden rise** in deaths from the disease between 1990 and 2000.

....

Try to consider the less obvious reasons for a rise.

....

Top Tips: Antibiotics are just great but they should be used with care as nobody wants a nasty superbug hanging around, bugging everyone. You need to know how these can develop. So learn it.

Antibiotics

Q4 There is concern about the appearance of **superbugs**.

a) Explain how microorganisms can develop **resistance** to an antibiotic.

....

....

b) Two things are thought to help combat superbugs:

> 1. Doctors should avoid prescribing antibiotics for minor ailments if patients can do without them.
>
> 2. When needed, doctors should provide a wide variety of antibiotics and not use a few all the time.

Explain how these actions **reduce** the chance of more superbugs appearing.

Action 1 ....

....

Action 2 ....

....

Q5 The graph shows the number of bacteria in Gary's blood during a two-week course of **antibiotics**.

Symptoms are present when the level of bacteria is above this line.

a) How long after starting the course of antibiotics will Gary's symptoms disappear? ....

b) Why is it important for Gary to **finish** his full course of antibiotics?

....

....

Drug Trials

Q1 Before a drug can be sold, it is tested on a variety of different cells and organisms. Put the cells and organisms in the order that drugs would be tested on. The first one has been done for you.

1 Human cells in a laboratory

☐ Sufferers of the disease

☐ Healthy human beings

☐ Mammals (other than humans)

Q2 Explain why, during drug trials, the following are usually tested on:

a) Live mammals.

....

b) Human cells grown in a lab.

....

Q3 Many people are **against** the use of animals for testing drugs intended for humans.

a) Give one **advantage** of testing drugs on animals.

....

b) Give one **disadvantage** of using animals, when the drug is intended for humans.

....

Q4 Before a drug is tested on sufferers, **clinical trials** are carried out with **healthy volunteers**.

a) Explain why healthy people are used to test the drug before the sufferers.

....

b) What does the term 'clinical trial' mean?

....

c) If the drug causes no problems whatsoever for the healthy volunteers, can scientists be certain that it is safe to use with sufferers? Explain your answer.

....

....

<u>Drug Trials</u>

Q5   An on-line advertisement for a new drug states that taking it can reduce 'bad' cholesterol by 52% (compared with 7% using a **placebo**) and increase 'good' cholesterol by 14% (compared with 3% using a placebo).

a)   What is a placebo?

....

b)   In trialling this drug, suggest why the manufacturer used a placebo.

....

c)   In a study of drug effectiveness it is essential for the people who take the drug and the people who take the placebo to have certain similar characteristics. Circle the characteristics that are important, as they could affect the results.

hair colour   age   income

marital status   health   sex

d)   Suggest why a placebo might not be used if the drug being tested was a possible cure for advanced cancer.

....

Q6   A new drug for a skin condition was being tested on patients that had the condition. The testers were using a '**double blind**' trial. Some of the patients were given a cream containing the drug, while others were given a placebo. Neither the patients nor the scientists were told which batch of cream had the drug in it.

a)   Why were the patients not told which cream they were given?

....

....

b)   Why were the scientists not told?

....

....

c)   If this drug is useful, suggest what results would you expect to see?

....

....

Top Tips: Testing drugs on animals is a very controversial issue. Some people think it's unethical and cruel to use animals in this way. Currently the law states that drugs must be tested on animals before they can be used on humans. A suitable alternative method is needed, before this can change.

The Circulatory System

Q1 Complete the passage using the words provided below.

carbon dioxide	vessels	nitrogen	oxygen	glucose
particles	veins	arteries	capillaries	tubes

Blood is vital to the working of the body. It is carried around the body in blood .... The blood is carried away from the heart in .... and brought back in .... It supplies the tissues with .... and .... for energy, and carries .... to the lungs, where it is removed.

Q2 The **heart** keeps blood pumping around the body.

a) Why is a blood supply to the heart (via the coronary arteries) essential?

....

b) What type of cell makes up the walls of the heart?

....

Q3 People are advised to lower the amount of **fat** in their diet to reduce the risk of **heart disease**.

How can too much fat in a diet lead to heart disease?

....

....

Q4 The pictures below show cross sections of two **blood vessels** — an artery and a vein.

a) Which blood vessel is an artery and which a vein?

A = ... B = ...

b) Explain how the following structures are related to the **function** of the blood vessel.

i) Strong and elastic walls of arteries ....

....

ii) Large lumen in veins ....

....

iii) Valves in veins ....

....

Module B2 — Keeping Healthy

<u>*Heart Disease*</u>

Q1 Each of the factors below **increase** the **risk** of heart disease. Tick the correct boxes to show whether the each of the factors are **lifestyle** factors or **non-lifestyle** factors.

	Lifestyle	Non-lifestyle
a) Poor diet	☐	☐
b) Excessive alcohol intake	☐	☐
c) Family history of heart disease	☐	☐
d) Smoking	☐	☐
e) Stress	☐	☐

Q2 State two reasons why **regular moderate exercise** reduces your risk of heart disease.

1. ....

2. ....

Q3 Heart disease is more common in **industrialised** countries than in **non-industrialised** countries. Tick the box next to the explanation(s) below that you think are valid, reasonable explanations for this.

☐ Poorer people in non-industrialised countries die of other things before they reach the age when heart disease is most likely.

☐ People in non-industrialised countries eat less junk food and so have a lower fat diet.

☐ Poorer people in non-industrialised countries will have to walk more because they cannot afford cars and so they get more exercise.

☐ Poorer people in non-industrialised countries cannot afford the treatment for heart disease and so are more likely to die of it.

Q4 Some scientists study the **patterns of disease** around the world and how diseases spread.

What name is given to this type of study?

....

Q5 Barry has been told that he has a high risk of heart disease because he is very overweight and does little exercise. However, he refuses to start an exercise programme and says "My father was even heavier than me and never did any exercise, and he lived until he was 80".

Explain what is wrong with Barry's argument.

....

....

Correlation and Cause

Q1 Read the passage below and answer the questions that follow.

In the UK today, around 13 million adults smoke cigarettes. The consequences to health of smoking are widely accepted, especially in relation to the increased risk of lung cancer. Heart disease is as great a problem but is often overlooked as a significant risk associated with smoking.

Heart disease is a major problem in Western Europe, with 268 000 heart attacks each year in the UK alone. A recent study has estimated that 29% of all heart attacks in Western Europe are due to smoking. Tobacco smoke contains around 4000 chemicals in the form of particles and gases, some of which are thought to have harmful effects on the body.

A 50 year study (study A) showed that mortality from heart disease in Britain was 60% higher in smokers than in non-smokers. The results of this study are shown in figure 1.

The study also looked at other diseases, such as cancers, in relation to smoking. Cancer is thought to be the most common form of death from smoking in the UK. The annual mortality rates from lung cancer are shown in figure 2 below for current and non-smokers.

Figure 1 Study A — Annual mortality per 100 000 men

Cause of death	Non smokers	Smokers
Lung cancer	14	209
All cancers	305	656
Coronary heart disease	573	892
All cardiovascular disease	1037	1643
Chronic obstructive lung disease	10	127
All respiratory disease	107	313
Total mortality	1706	3038

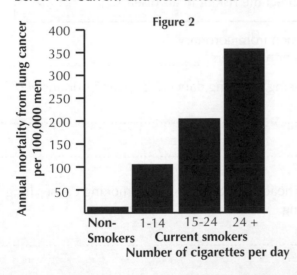

Figure 2

The study concluded that about half of all regular smokers will be killed by their habit. However the ill effects of smoking are not only felt by smokers themselves but also by those around them. Inhaling second-hand smoke can also be harmful to health. It is thought that regular exposure to second-hand smoke increases the risk of heart disease and lung cancer by around 25%.

A significant proportion of the UK population are regularly exposed to second-hand smoke in the home — around 7.3 million adults and 5 million children. There is mounting evidence that this can have a serious effect on health. Many potentially toxic gases are thought to be present in higher concentrations in second-hand smoke than in the 'mainstream' smoke inhaled by smokers. These gases include ammonia and hydrogen cyanide. However, only two thirds of British adults believe that passive smoking increases the risk of heart disease.

It is becoming clear that there needs to be an increase in awareness in the risks of smoking in relation to heart disease, as well as the general long term effects of passive smoking.

Module B2 — Keeping Healthy

Correlation and Cause

a) What percentage of heart attacks in Western Europe are thought to be due to smoking? Circle the correct answer.

25%   29%   50%   60%

b) Explain why should you include as many people as possible in a study of the effects of smoking.

....

....

c) **i)** Suggest another group of people that it would have been helpful to include in study A. Give a reason for your answer.

....

....

ii) Complete the passage below choosing from the words provided.

minimise	exercise	body weight	maximise	height

Studies like this must try to .... the effects of other factors.

Things like the .... of people in the study and the amount of

.... they do could also effect the risk of heart disease.

d) How many more deaths per year per 100 000 men from coronary heart disease are there in smokers compared to non smokers? ....

e) Does figure 2 show a **correlation** between smoking and lung cancer? Explain your answer.

....

....

f) A newspaper reported these findings under the headline, "Studies show smoking causes lung cancer". Explain why this headline is misleading.

....

....

g) At the moment there is a ban on smoking in public buildings in some countries, but exceptions are allowed. Many people want a complete ban.

i) Suggest one reason that would be given by campaigners for a complete ban.

....

ii) Suggest one reason that would be given for those that oppose such a ban.

....

....

Natural and Synthetic Materials

Q1   Draw lines to match up each object with the probable source of the material used to make it.

paper

leather coat

car tyre

silk

silkworm larva

beech tree

cows

rubber tree

Q2   Complete the statements below using the following words:

| two | element | four | ions | atoms | material | mixed | bonded | mixture |

a) All materials are made up of ....

b) An .... is a chemical made up of one type of atom.

c) Compounds are chemicals made up of .... or more different elements .... together.

d) A .... contains two or more individual substances that are not chemically joined together.

Q3   Give an advantage of the following **synthetic** items compared to the **natural** alternatives.

a) Rubber seals: ....

b) Clothes: ....

c) Paints: ....

Q4   Tick the boxes to show whether the following statements are **true** or **false**.

	True	False
a) One advantage of using a synthetic material is that you can control its properties during manufacture.	☐	☐
b) It's always more expensive to use synthetic materials rather than the natural substance.	☐	☐
c) The pigment in paint is usually a natural material.	☐	☐

Top Tips: Even though all materials are made up chemicals, some materials are natural and others are synthetic. Make sure you know the difference between these — natural materials are made from living things such as plants and animals, and synthetic materials are made by humans.

Materials and Properties

Q1   Complete the statements below by circling the correct words.

a)   A **weak** / **strong** material is good at resisting a force.

b)   You can tell how strong a material is by gradually applying a force to a sample of the material until it breaks or is **temporarily** / **permanently** deformed.

c)   High tensile strength is when a material can resist **pulling** / **pushing** forces.

d)   Poor compressive strength means low resistance to **pulling** / **pushing** forces.

e)   Climbing ropes need a **low** / **high** tensile strength, whereas a brick low down in a wall needs a high **tensile** / **compressive** strength to resist the **weight** / **mass** of the bricks above it.

Q2   Complete the table by stating if each substance is a **liquid** or a **solid** at room temperature (20 °C).

Substance	Water	Sulfur	Propanone	Sodium chloride
Melting point (°C)	0	115	-95	801
Boiling point (°C)	100	444	56	1413
State at room temperature				

Q3   Answer the following questions about the properties of materials.

a)   Explain why it is possible for a bendy material to be strong.

....

b)   Steel is very stiff. Suggest why steel rods are put inside concrete posts.

....

c)   Why are diamond tips used on industrial drills?

....

Q4   Use the following densities to answer the questions below.

Gold 19.3 g/cm³	Iron 7.9 g/cm³	Concrete 2.6 g/cm³
Cork 0.25 g/cm³	Pine 0.5 g/cm³	Mahogany 0.8 g/cm³

a)   What is the difference between density and mass?

....

b)   Which materials from the list will sink when placed in water? (Water density = 1.0 g/cm³)

....

c)   What will happen if a large piece of mahogany is put in a bath of water?

....

<u>Making Measurements</u>

Q1   Andrew and Mark conducted similar experiments to find out how **temperature** affects the **rate** of a reaction. They mixed 10 cm³ of sodium thiosulfate solution with 10 cm³ of hydrochloric acid solution to form a yellow precipitate of sulfur. The experiment involved timing how long it took for a black cross to 'disappear' through the resulting cloudy liquid.

The experiment was repeated for solutions at different temperatures. Both students followed the same method. The tables below show their results.

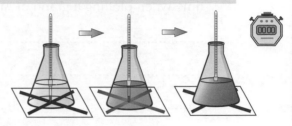

Andrew

Temperature (ºC)	Time (s)			
	Trial 1	Trial 2	Trial 3	Average
20	55	59	57	
30	32	31	33	
40	21	20	19	
50	13	14	13	
60	9	8	10	

Mark

Temperature (ºC)	Time (s)
20	56
30	54
40	22
50	14
60	10

a)   Which pupil is likely to have the more accurate results? Explain your answer.

....

....

b)   Give three ways in which they could have made sure that their experiments were fair tests.

....

....

....

c)   Complete Andrew's results table by working out the average time taken at each temperature.

d)   Andrew was told that the cross disappeared when 1000 mg of sulfur was formed. He can calculate **speed of the reaction** by dividing 1000 by the average time for the reaction. The units will be mg/s. For each temperature, calculate the speed of the reaction.

....

....

....

....

Making Measurements

e) **i)** On the grid, plot a graph of Andrew's results. Use the average time at each temperature.

ii) Suggest why it is a good idea to use the average time when plotting a graph of Andrew's results.

....

....

....

iii) Describe the correlation between temperature and time.

....

iv) What conclusion can be drawn from Andrew's results?

....

f) Compare Andrew and Mark's results.

i) Which of Mark's results appears to be an outlier?

....

ii) Explain your choice.

....

....

iii) Suggest how Mark could be sure that this result is an outlier.

....

iv) Suggest two things that may have caused an error in Mark's results.

....

....

v) At which temperature is there the greatest range in Andrew's results?

....

Materials, Properties and Uses

Q1 For each of the following questions, choose the most likely letter from the list below.

   A diving suit **B** milk carton **C** window pane **D** washing line

a) To which use would you put a low density opaque plastic that is hard and strong? ....

b) To which use would you put nylon fibres that are flexible with high tensile strength? ....

c) To which use would you put neoprene (waterproof, strong, but soft and flexible)? ....

d) To which use would you put polycarbonate (strong, hard and transparent)? ....

Q2 Match the following sentences with their correct endings.

Gold is suitable for jewellery because...

uPVC is suitable for guttering pipes because...

Stainless steel is suitable for knives and forks because...

Lead is suitable for paperweights because...

...it is stiff.

...it is shiny.

...it has a high density.

...it is non-toxic.

Q3 The properties of different materials make them suitable for different applications.

a) Explain why a tennis racket is made with a **metal frame** and **nylon strings**.

....

....

b) Explain why a saucepan is made with **a metal body** and **wooden handle**.

....

....

Q4 A mystery material has just been discovered. It has a **high melting point**, **high tensile strength** and **low density**, and is also **flexible**, **soft**, **non-toxic** and **flame resistant**.

a) Put a ring around the product that this material would be most suitable for.

   knives and forks   guttering   children's nightwear   synthetic candle wax

b) Explain how one of the properties of the 'mystery' substance make it suitable for your choice.

....

c) For one of the other products give two reasons why the mystery material would **not** be suitable.

   1. ....

   2. ....

Chemical Synthesis

Q1 Tick the boxes to show whether the statements are **true** or **false**.

True False

a) Fossil fuels are formed from dead plants and animals.

b) Hydrocarbons contain carbon and water only.

c) Most of the crude oil we extract is used for providing energy.

d) Long-chain hydrocarbons are quite viscous.

e) Cracking is the process of making longer hydrocarbons.

Q2 Complete the following passage by choosing from the words below.

varying   synthetic   mixture   chains   modified   natural
compounds   equal   diesel   plastics   refines   small

Crude oil is a .... of lots of different hydrocarbons. These molecules are

.... of atoms of .... lengths. The petrochemical industry

.... crude oil to produce petrol, ... and

other fuels and lubricants. A very .... amount of the crude oil is used

to make .... substances — man-made .... such as

............................, medicines and fertilisers.

Q3 Bob runs an **oil refinery plant**. He is comparing the percentages of each fraction produced in his plant with his customers' demand. His results are shown in the table.

Fraction	Refinery gas	Petrol and naphtha	Kerosene	Diesel	Oil and Bitumen
% of production	3	15	12	21	49
% of demand	5	28	9	24	34

a) Which fractions are currently in greater demand than is available?

....

b) What is likely to be the greatest use of these fractions?

....

c) Which fractions are likely to be 'cracked'?

....

Top Tips: Crude oil is a mixture of hydrocarbons, and it's a pretty useless substance on its own. However, refined crude oil is useful for loads of different things because each fraction has different properties. They can be cracked to produce even more of the useful substances.

Module C2 — Material Choices

Polymerisation

Q1   For each of the following questions give the most likely answer from A–D.

a)   Polymerisation is best described as ....

A lots of small molecules joining to form long chains

B lots of large molecules joining to form long chains

C a small number of molecules joining together

D two molecules joining together to form one molecule

b)   Polymers are among the most important .... materials.

A synthetic   B biodegradable   C natural   D black

c)   Polymers are usually .... based.

A sodium   B sulfur   C carbon   D argon

d)   Polymers are formed when small molecules are mixed under conditions of .... pressure.

A low   B medium   C high   D zero

Q2   The uses of polymers depend on their properties.

a)   Suggest three properties that a polymer used to make window frames should have.

....

b)   Give two properties of high density polythene which make it suitable for washing-up bowls.

....

c)   Suggest why polystyrene foam is used for disposable tea cups.

....

d)   Give three properties of polypropene which make it suitable for use in plastic kettles.

....

Q3   Over time, materials used to make common items are replaced with more suitable materials.

a)   Suggest two advantages of using PET rather than glass for fizzy drink bottles.

....

....

b)   Suggest two advantages of replacing paper bags with plastic bags.

....

....

Structures and Properties of Polymers

Q1   Complete the following passage by circling the correct words.

> Polymer chains are held **together** / **apart** by forces between the chains. If these
> forces are weak, the chains **cannot** / **can** slide over each other easily. This makes
> the polymer **inflexible** / **flexible** and gives it a **low** / **high** melting point. The stronger
> the bonds between the polymer chains, the **more** / **less** energy is needed to break
> them apart, and the **lower** / **higher** the melting point.

Q2   Polymers can be **modified** to give them different properties.

   a) In what four ways can polymers be modified to change their properties?

   1. ....   2. ....

   3. ....   4. ....

   b) How could you lower the melting point of a polymer?

   ....

   c) Describe how a polymer's properties would change if its chain length was increased.

   ....

   ....

   d) Explain how adding cross-linking agents affects the properties of a polymer.

   ....

   ....

Q3   uPVC is strong, durable and rigid. When another chemical is added to the uPVC, it
          becomes stretchy, soft and easier to shape. It can then be used as **synthetic leather**.

   a) What is the general name given to chemicals that can be added to polymers to make them softer
          and more pliable?

   ....

   b) Explain how these chemicals make the polymer softer.

   ....

   ....

Structures and Properties of Polymers

Q4   Read the following passage and then answer the questions.

In America in the early 1830s natural rubber was used to make various things. However, in hot weather it turned into a glue-like mess as it 'melted'. Charles Goodyear experimented by adding different substances to the rubber to try to improve its properties. By accident, he found that heating rubber with sulfur produced a hardened version of the rubber. He called the process vulcanization and set up a business making tyres.

a)   What is the process of hardening rubber by adding sulfur called?

....

b)   What is the cross-linking agent in this process?

....

c)   Describe how adding a cross-linking agent changed the properties of the rubber.

....

....

Q5   Polymers can have a **crystalline** or a **non-crystalline** structure.

a)   State whether the diagrams show a crystalline or a non-crystalline plastic.

i)

ii)

....

b)   Describe the structure of a non-crystalline polymer.

....

....

c)   Describe the structure of a crystalline polymer.

....

....

d)   Give three properties of crystalline polymers.

....

Top Tips: A polymer's properties depend on how its chains are arranged and how they're held together. But — don't forget that polymers can be modified to change their properties. You'd better get modifying the contents of your brain to include this stuff, 'cos this could come up in the exam...

Module C2 — Material Choices

Life Cycle Assessments

Q1 Complete the passage using the words below.

Each word can only be used once.

stage	cycle	environment	assess	laws	governments
sustainable		process	materials	protect	cost

The business of manufacturing things is changing as new .... are

being introduced. Companies have to .... the impact their processes

and products will have on the .... and use this information to choose

a .... that does minimal harm. It also helps them to choose the best

.... for the job. They have to look at the impact of each

.... of the product's life — this is known as a Life ....

Assessment. Data from the Life Cycle Assessment enables companies to help

.... future generations.

Q2 Which stages of a product's life are being described below? Match them up.

A computer being powered by electricity.

Using the product.

Polythene being made from ethene.

Disposing of the product.

A lot of plastic bottles being thrown away.

Extracting the raw materials.

Oil being drilled out of the ground.

Manufacturing the product.

Q3 Tick the boxes to show whether the statements are **true** or **false**.

                                                                                                                                           True **False**

a) A Life Cycle Assessment can't help in deciding the best raw materials to use. ☐ ☐

b) Generally, the extraction of raw materials needs energy. ☐ ☐

c) Companies always include cost as one of the factors to think about. ☐ ☐

d) The quantity of available raw materials should be ignored in an Life Cycle Assessment. ☐ ☐

e) Recycling materials at the disposal stage is more sustainable than putting them in landfill. ☐ ☐

Life Cycle Assessments

Q4 Governments in poorer countries are often less strict about environmental concerns when manufacturing products.

Suggest a reason for this.

....

....

Q5 The length of a product's life cycle can vary quite a bit.

Compare a plastic drinks bottle with a plastic garden chair.

a) Which product is likely to have the longest life-span?

....

b) Which product is likely to cost more to manufacture?

....

c) Which product is more likely to be recycled rather than being put into landfill?

....

Q6 A Life Cycle Assessment can tell a company if it's possible to make a product and what the environmental impact will be. However, it can't tell the company whether it **should** make the product.

Suggest two other things that companies may consider when deciding whether to manufacture a product.

....

....

....

Q7 Suggest three benefits a company might get from doing a Life Cycle Assessment.

1. ....

2. ....

3. ....

Top Tips: Life Cycle Assessments do just what you'd expect them to do — they look at each stage of the life cycle of a potential product to assess the impact that it would have on the environment. Get that sorted and it'll be one less assessment to think about...

Module C2 — Material Choices

Module P2 — Radiation and Life

Electromagnetic Radiation

Q1 Which statement best describes what we mean by **radiation**?
Circle the correct letter.

    A   An invisible substance that causes cancer

    B   Something that travels as photon atoms

    C   The transfer of energy from a source

    D   The waste products of a nuclear bomb

Q2 There are seven types of electromagnetic radiation which make up a continuous **spectrum**.

a) Complete the electromagnetic spectrum below.

			visible light			gamma rays

b) Electromagnetic radiation transfers energy as **photons**.

    i) What is a photon? ....

    ii) What's the difference between a **microwave** photon and a **gamma ray** photon?

    ....

c) Which has higher energy photons? (Circle the correct option in each case.)

    i)   microwaves   ultraviolet

    ii)   violet light   red light   *Think of where ultraviolet and infrared are on the EM spectrum.*

    iii)   gamma rays   ultraviolet

Q3 The Sun emits radiation from all parts of the EM spectrum. The graph shows how the **intensity** (brightness) of radiation from the Sun varies with the **energy** of the photons.

a) What is the energy of the photons of the brightest radiation?

    .... J

b) Which is more intense — red light from the Sun or violet light from the Sun?

    ....

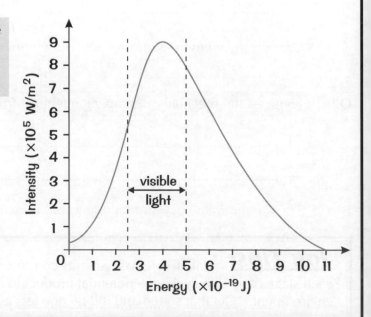

EM Radiation and Energy

Q1 Match up the terms and their definitions below. You won't need to use all the definitions.

source

reflection

transmission

absorption

detector

radiation passes through an object or a vacuum

radiation is 'stopped' by the object and the energy is deposited

an object that allows radiation to pass through it

radiation 'bounces' off an object

an object that absorbs and registers radiation

an object that emits radiation

Q2 A laser emits **2 J** of light energy. The energy of each photon in the laser beam is **2.8 × 10⁻¹⁹ J**.

a) How many photons are emitted? ....

b) If twice this number of photons were produced,
how much **energy** would the laser emit? ....

c) A different laser emits photons with an energy of 5 × 10⁻¹⁹ J. How will the light
produced by this laser look **different** from the light produced by the first one?

....

Q3 The photons in **red** and **blue** light have different **energies**.

> Look at a diagram of the EM spectrum and photon energy...

a) Fill in the blanks to complete the sentence below:

The total energy produced by a radiation source depends on the ....

of the photons and the .... **of photons it emits.**

b) If a red laser and a blue laser produce the same
number of photons, which delivers more **energy**? ....

c) If both lasers deliver the same total amount of energy, which
has produced more **photons**? Circle the correct answer.   **red laser   blue laser**

Q4 How 'bright' a beam of light appears depends on its **intensity**.

a) Explain what's meant by the **intensity** of electromagnetic radiation, in terms of energy.

....

b) Two planets, Yurg and Zorg, orbit the same star.

i) Continue the paths of the photons produced by the star.

ii) Explain why **Yurg** is much **hotter** than Zorg.

Yurg

Zorg

photons emitted
by the star

....

....

Module P2 — Radiation and Life

Ionisation

Q1 Some types of electromagnetic radiation can be dangerous because they are **ionising**.

a) Describe what ionising radiation can do to an atom.

....

b) List the three types of ionising electromagnetic radiation.

....

c) Explain why only these types of EM radiation can cause ionisation.

....

Q2 The diagram shows a molecule being ionised. Label the **photon**, the **molecule** and the **ions**.

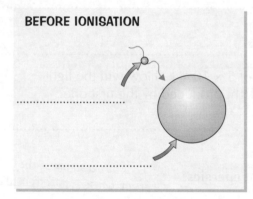

BEFORE IONISATION

....

....

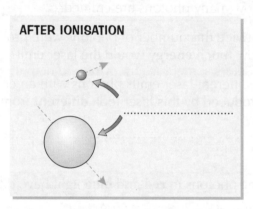

AFTER IONISATION

....

Q3 Choose words from the list to complete the paragraph about the effects of ionising radiation.

radiation   grow   cells   ions   mutations   acid   DNA
divide   damage   low   kill   high   reactions   cancer

If ionising radiation hits molecules in your ...., it can turn them

into .... Ions can damage .... molecules

in the cells, which can cause .... If this happens, the cell could

start to .... uncontrollably — this is ....

Very high doses of radiation can .... some of your cells, causing

.... sickness.

Top Tips: All EM radiation is the same sort of thing, but the different types have different
properties, and some are more dangerous than others. It's the ionising types that can do really serious
damage — you need to know what ionisation does to molecules, and the effects on the body's cells.

Module P2 — Radiation and Life

Ionisation

Q4 The Sun emits radiation in all parts of the EM spectrum, including **ultraviolet (UV)**.

a) Why do we need to protect ourselves from too much UV radiation from the Sun?

....

b) **i)** Complete the sentence by underlining the correct word.

Sun-screens can protect us from the Sun's rays by **absorbing** / **reflecting** UV radiation.

ii) Describe two other ways you can protect yourself from the Sun's UV radiation.

....

c) On sunny days, skiers often get sun burnt on their **chins**.
Suggest an explanation for this.

....

....

Simon found
that a false beard was
very effective protection.

Q5 Doctors sometimes use **X-rays** to help them diagnose a patient's injury or illness.

a) Taking X-rays involves risks for both patients and hospital staff.
Hospitals try to minimise these risks according to the ALARA principle.

i) Explain what the 'ALARA principle' means.

....

ii) Explain why the radiographer taking an X-ray wears a lead apron but the patient doesn't.

....

....

iii) Describe what measures radiographers take to reduce the risk **to the patient**.

....

b) Most people are prepared to have X-rays taken, even though this involves a slightly
increased risk of developing cancer in later life. Suggest why, in terms of:

i) balancing the real risks and benefits to the patient.

....

....

ii) how the patient perceives the risk.

....

....

Some Uses of EM Radiation

Q1 EM radiation can be used to **transmit information**.
Write down two **devices** which use the following types of radiation.

a) radio waves

....

b) microwaves

....

c) infrared

....

Q2 Conventional and microwave ovens both use EM radiation.

a) What type of EM radiation does a conventional oven use to cook food? ....

b) Emma bakes a potato in her microwave oven.
Describe how the microwaves affect the water molecules in the potato.

....

c) Emma loves sponge puddings. These are the cooking instructions on the packaging
of her favourite microwaveable 'luxury double chocolate sponge' pudding.

Power of Oven:	650 W	750 W	850 W
Cooking time:	150 s	135 s	120 s

i) Explain why the time needed to heat up the pudding varies for the different ovens.

....

....

ii) Which of these ovens produces the most intense microwaves?
Circle the correct answer.

650 W   750 W   850 W

d) Emma puts an empty plastic cup in her microwave and turns it on for 20 seconds at full power.
Explain why the plastic cup doesn't get any hotter.

....

....

....

Some Uses of EM Radiation

Q3 State two features of microwave ovens that prevent microwaves from **leaking** out.

1. ....

2. ....

Q4 Some people worry that microwaves from **mobile phones** might be bad for their health.

a) What effect do microwaves have on living cells?

....

b) Why is using a mobile phone safer than putting your head into an operating microwave oven?

....

c) Is there any conclusive evidence that the microwaves from mobile phones cause cancer?

....

d) Apart from people using their phones, who else might be at risk from the microwave radiation used by mobile phone networks?

....

....

Q5 A scientific report for the UK government said that there was no evidence that the radiation from mobile phones was harmful, but recommended that children should limit their use of mobiles.

a) Even though there's currently no evidence of harm, why should we still be careful about how much we use our mobile phones?

....

....

b) If we aren't certain about the risks of something which **might** cause serious harm, it's sensible to try and avoid it. What do we call this principle? (Circle one of A-D.)

    A   The reactionary principle

    B   The safe principle

    C   The precautionary principle

    D   The preventative principle

BEWARE
There is a risk
that this dog will
lick you.

> ***Top Tips:*** Using your mobile phone is probably **not that risky** compared to, say, crossing a busy road. But at the moment we're just **not sure** about it — mobiles haven't been used for long enough for us to find out. Cars have been around for a while though — we know they're dangerous.

EM Radiation and Life

Q1 Electromagnetic radiation from the Sun is very important for life on Earth.

a) Fill in the gaps using some of the words in the list below.

transmitting	visible light	ultraviolet	absorbing	liquids	gases	reflecting

The Sun emits all types of electromagnetic radiation. However, various

.... in the atmosphere filter out some of this radiation by

.... or .... it. One type of

radiation that passes through the atmosphere easily is ....

b) Complete the sentence below by underlining the correct word.

The Earth's surface heats up during the day because it **reflects / absorbs / emits** EM radiation.

Q2 Green plants make their own 'food' — glucose — by **photosynthesis**. The process of **respiration** then releases energy from the glucose.

a) Fill in the table to show which gases are added to or removed from the atmosphere during these processes.

	Respiration	Photosynthesis
Gas added to atmosphere		
Gas removed from atmosphere		

b) Give two reasons why photosynthesis is vital for the survival of human beings.

1. ....

2. ....

Q3 The graph shows how the **rate of photosynthesis** in a particular plant depends on **temperature**.

a) What conclusion can you draw from the graph?

....

....

b) Give two reasons why the Sun is important for photosynthesis.

....

....

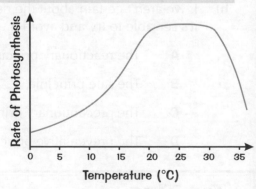

EM Radiation and The Atmosphere

Q1   The diagram below shows how the 'greenhouse effect' keeps the Earth warm.
Use the descriptions **A** to **E** to label the diagram. The first one has been done for you.

A
The Earth absorbs radiation from the Sun.

B
The Earth emits heat radiation.

C
Greenhouse gases absorb radiation from Earth.

E
The greenhouse gases emit some heat radiation into space.

D
The greenhouse gases emit some heat towards Earth.

Q2   Which of the statements below is the best description of the **greenhouse effect**? Circle A, B, C or D.

A   Global warming caused by man's impact on the environment.

B   A process which keeps the Earth warmer than it would otherwise be.

C   A chemical reaction in the atmosphere which releases heat energy.

D   The natural heating effect of the Sun.

Q3   Tick the boxes next to any **greenhouse gases** below.

nitrogen ☐   water vapour ☐   carbon dioxide ☐

oxygen ☐   methane ☐   helium ☐

Q4   One 'layer' of the atmosphere has a high concentration of **ozone** — the 'ozone layer'.

a)   Explain briefly why the ozone layer is important for living organisms on Earth.

....

b)   Ozone is an oxygen molecule with the formula O_3.
'Normal' oxygen molecules have the formula O_2.

i)   What happens to an **oxygen** molecule when it absorbs **UV** radiation?

....

ii)   Explain how this leads to the formation of ozone. ....

....

iii)   What happens to an **ozone** molecule when it absorbs UV radiation?

....

The Carbon Cycle

Q1   The diagram shows the **carbon cycle**.

a)   How is carbon removed from the atmosphere?

....

b)   Humans are currently cutting down and burning trees from vast areas of rainforest.

i)   What effect is this having on the amount of carbon dioxide in the atmosphere?

....

ii)   Give two reasons for this effect.

1. ....

2. ....

c)   Humans are burning oil, coal and natural gas to provide energy. Before we did this, what processes allowed carbon to be released back into the atmosphere?

....

d)   **i)**   What are decomposers? ....

ii)   Explain their role in the carbon cycle.

....

Q2   For thousands of years the concentration of carbon dioxide in the Earth's atmosphere was approximately **constant**.

a)   Circle the letter next to the best explanation for why this was.

A   No carbon dioxide was added and no carbon dioxide was removed.

B   Carbon dioxide was added and removed in equal quantities.

C   The temperature was too cold for photosynthesis.

b)   Over the past 200 years, the concentration of carbon dioxide has **not** been stable.

i)   Describe how the atmospheric CO_2 concentration changed over this period.

....

ii)   Give two reasons why this change has been occurring.

....

....

....

....

Module P2 — Radiation and Life

Climate Change

Q1 Complete the passage by choosing from the words below.

fallen	clouds	carbon	pressures	greenhouse
temperatures	increased	butterfly	sulfur	sea

Global .... have .... in recent
years. This is due to an increased .... effect caused
by 'too much' .... dioxide in the atmosphere.

Q2 Below are five statements about climate change.
Tick the boxes to show which statements are **descriptions
of data** and which are possible **explanations of data**.

Description of Data   Explanation of Data

a) Global temperatures are steadily increasing. ☐ ☐

b) Carbon dioxide levels in the atmosphere are steadily increasing. ☐ ☐

c) The rise in atmospheric carbon dioxide
concentration is causing a rise in global temperatures. ☐ ☐

d) There are more extreme weather events every year. ☐ ☐

e) The Earth's increasingly extreme weather is caused by global warming. ☐ ☐

Q3 Map A shows the coastline
of Great Britain **now**. Map B
shows how it might look **in a
thousand years' time**.

Map A    **Map B**

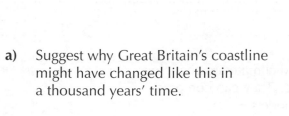

a) Suggest why Great Britain's coastline
might have changed like this in
a thousand years' time.

....

b) Give two ways in which the **warming** of the Earth would cause this effect.

1. ....

2. ....

Top Tips: You need to know about the possible consequences of global warming and
climate change. It's not just so you can pass exams — serious changes could happen in your lifetime.

Climate Change

Q4   **Climate** means the **general long-term weather conditions** in a region. E.g. Ireland has a wet climate — it gets lots of rain throughout the year, and it's been like this for hundreds of years.

a)   If Ireland's climate changed to become drier, suggest how this might affect farmers in Ireland.

....

....

b)   Many scientists think that climate change will also involve more cases of **extreme weather**.

    i)   Give two examples of 'extreme weather' events.

      ....

    ii)   Central Africa has a generally very **dry** climate. Farmers rely on heavy rains during one part of the year to provide enough water for their crops and animals.

      Suggest one way that climate change might affect people living here.

      ....

      ....

      ....

Q5   Scientists use **climate models** to predict how the Earth's climate will change.

a)   Professor Cloud has developed a new climate model. She tests it by putting in some data about the climate as it was 10 years ago, and getting the model to predict the present day climate.

Explain how this helps Professor Cloud know whether her new climate model is any good.

....

....

b)   Climate scientists monitor how the atmosphere and climate are changing by collecting data on temperatures, CO_2 levels, etc. They can compare this data to the results predicted by their climate models.

Climate models show that the current 'global warming' **isn't** caused by **natural changes**.

What is meant by 'natural changes'?

....

....

....

Risks from EM Radiation

Q1   Read the article below and answer the questions which follow it.

> About 70 000 people in the UK develop skin cancer every year, and doctors expect this number to rise. Some people are particularly at risk, especially those with fair skin. This is because fair skin doesn't contain much melanin — a brown pigment which is a natural barrier to UV radiation.
>
> To minimise the risk of harm, people are advised to limit the amount of time they spend in bright sunshine. When you *are* out in the sun, you can reduce the risk of skin damage by keeping covered up or applying sun-screen.
>
> The Met Office produces a five day 'UV index' forecast. You can use the table below to estimate your personal risk of damage from the Sun:
>
> | UV Index | Fair skin (burns) | Fair skin (tans) | Brown skin | Black skin |
> |----------|-------------------|------------------|------------|------------|
> | 1, 2 | Low | Low | Low | Low |
> | 3, 4 | Medium | Low | Low | Low |
> | 5 | High | Medium | Low | Low |
> | 6 | Very high | Medium | Medium | Low |
> | 7, 8, 9 | Very high | High | Medium | Medium |
> | 10 | Very high | High | High | Medium |

a)   **i)**   The population of the UK is about 60 million. What percentage of UK residents develop skin cancer in any one year?

....

   ii)   Suggest why your answer above might not be very helpful for an individual trying to understand their own risk of developing skin cancer.

....

....

b)   By referring to the table, state two factors that increase the risk of skin cancer. For each one, outline a plausible mechanism to explain why the risk is increased.

1. Factor: .... Mechanism: ....

....

2. Factor: .... Mechanism: ....

....

c)   On sunny days, some fair-skinned people stay in the sun for long periods of time, even though they've heard that this could be harmful. Suggest two reasons why.

1. ....

2. ....

Risks from EM Radiation

Q2 Read the article below and answer the questions which follow it.

There's no doubt that carbon dioxide levels in the atmosphere are rising. Sensors at an observatory on the top of Mauna Loa (a mountain in Hawaii) have measured a rise from 315 to over 380 parts per million of carbon dioxide since the 1950s. There's a scientific consensus that this has caused a rise in the average global temperature.

To investigate the distant past, scientists have drilled into the ice in Antarctica, obtaining samples from thousands of metres below the surface. The ice at these depths was formed from snow which fell hundreds of thousands of years ago.

As snow falls it traps tiny bubbles of air. Scientists can analyse these bubbles in the ice samples to work out the CO_2 level and temperature at the time the ice formed. The graph shows some of this data.

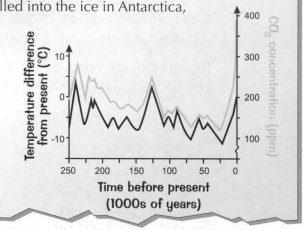

a) Why do scientists need to examine data for hundreds of thousands of years to investigate the relationship between temperature and carbon dioxide levels?

....

b) **i)** Explain why the data from Antarctic ice samples alone doesn't prove that rising carbon dioxide levels have caused global warming.

....

....

ii) Give an example, unrelated to global warming, of two factors which are correlated but where neither factor causes the other.

....

c) Many scientists are trying to persuade governments to follow the 'precautionary principle' when making decisions related to global warming. Describe one way we would have to change our behaviour if the precautionary principle was followed.

....

....

d) Explain why scientists accept there is a **causal link** between carbon dioxide levels and global temperatures.

....

....

Evolution

Q1 Life on **Earth** is incredibly **varied**.

a) How long ago is life on Earth thought to have begun? Circle the correct answer.

350 thousand years   3500 million years   (3500 billion years)

b) How many species are there **estimated** to be on Earth today? Circle the correct answer.

less than 1 million   (2 - 100 million)   200 - 1000 million

c) Circle the correct word in each pair to complete the following sentence.

The species on Earth today grew / (evolved) from very (simple) / complex living things.

d) Many more species have existed on Earth since life began than are around today. What has happened to the species that no longer exist?

Extiction

Q2 The **theory of Evolution** is generally accepted in the scientific community because there is good **evidence** to support it.

a) How much **DNA** do humans and chimpanzees share? Circle the correct answer.

15%   55%   (95%)

b) Chickens share 60% of their DNA with humans. Compare this with your answer to part a) to explain how DNA evidence supports the theory of evolution.

....

....

c) i) Give another source of evidence for evolution. ....

ii) Explain how this evidence supports the theory.

....

Q3 No one knows for sure how **life** on Earth **began**.

a) One theory is that all life evolved from **simple chemicals**. What property would these chemicals need to have in order for them to develop into living species?

....

b) Suggest two places that these chemicals could have come from.

1. ....

2. ....

c) Suggest a reason why there is no definite answer for how life on Earth began.

....

Natural Selection

Q1 Describe the difference between **natural selection** and **evolution**.

....

....

Q2 Tick the boxes to show whether the following statements are **true** or **false**.

                                                             True   **False**

a) Species become better and better suited to an environment due to natural selection. ☐   ☐

b) Organisms with a better chance of survival are less likely to pass on their genes. ☐   ☐

Q3 The statements below explain the **process** of natural selection. Number the statements to put them in the correct order. The first and last stages have been done for you.

☐	This means more of the next generation have the alleles which help them survive.
☐	These organisms have a better chance of survival.
1	Living things vary slightly from each other.
☐	The species becomes better and better able to survive in its environment.
7	Over several generations, the most advantageous features are naturally selected.
☐	Some variations make an organism better suited to its environment.
☐	The organisms which are more likely to survive are more likely to breed and pass on their genes.

Q4 **Variation** within a species is needed for natural selection.

a) What two factors can cause variation?

....

b) Which of these factors can be passed on to future generations?

....

Q5 A farmer wants to produce large red tomatoes because these make the most money. He cross-breeds two varieties — one that produces large, orangey-red tomatoes, and another that produces smaller, bright red fruit.

a) What should the farmer do when he next comes to breed new tomato plants?

....

b) **i)** What is the process the farmer is using called? ....

    ii) How is it different from natural selection? ....

....

Producing New Species

Q1 Mutations happen all the time, but rarely produce new species.

a) What are mutations?

....

b) Suggest two factors that might cause mutations.

....

c) Mutations that are passed on to the next generation may have an effect in the offspring, or no effect at all. Explain how a mutation could cause the following results:

i) **No** effect ....

ii) A **harmful** effect ....

iii) A **positive** effect ....

Q2 Helen has skin cancer caused by a mutation that **damaged the DNA** in her skin cells. Since she developed cancer, Helen has had three children. None of her children have skin cancer.

Explain why the mutation was **not** passed from Helen to her children.

....

....

Q3 Many years ago, a population of finches lived on North Island where **small** seeds were plentiful. During a severe storm, some of the finches were blown to the neighbouring South Island where the seeds were generally **larger**.

a) The data below shows the population of finches with large and small beaks on each island 100 years after finches were first recorded on South Island. Draw lines to connect the data with the correct island.

80% large beaks, 20% small beaks

North Island

15% large beaks, 85% small beaks

South Island

b) Explain how and why the populations on the two islands have developed differently.

....

....

....

c) What environmental factor helped the two populations develop into separate species?

....

Producing New Species

Q4   Completely new species occasionally develop when certain factors combine.

a)   Which **three** of these factors can help to produce a new species? Circle the correct answers.

velocity   environmental change   mutations

predictions   extinctions   natural selection

b)   Explain how each of the factors you chose can contribute to the development of a new species.

1. ....

2. ....

3. ....

Q5   There are two varieties of **peppered moth** — one with light wings with dark spots, and one with dark wings and light spots. The graph below shows the population of each type of moth found in woodland near Manchester.

a)   Briefly describe how the population of the two types changed over the time shown on the graph.

i)   Light moth: ....

....

ii)   Dark moth: ....

....

b)   It is thought that the changes in the population sizes resulted from pollution from the Industrial Revolution darkening the bark of trees.

i)   Which type of moth would be better hidden from predators by darker trees? ....

ii)   Explain how this might have led to the change in population sizes seen on the graph.

....

....

....

c)   If the Industrial Revolution hadn't occurred, would the population sizes of the two moth species still have changed? Explain your answer.

....

....

> ***Top Tips:***   Mutations sound like they're straight out of science-fiction — when really they happen all the time without anyone noticing. Very rarely, though, new species do develop — but they tend to be only a little different from the old one. I can't see anyone making a film about that.

A Scientific Controversy

Q1   Complete the following passage by choosing the correct words from those given.

accepted   unchangeable   foolishness   creative   imagination   changeable

> Darwin had the ...*imagination*... to see beyond the idea that species
> were ...*changeable*... He made careful observations of species on
> the Galapagos islands and applied ...*creative*... thinking to come
> up with the idea of natural selection.

Q2   Tick the boxes to show whether the following statements about evolution are based on **data** or are part of an **explanation**.

	Data	Explanation
a) Fossils from related animals have been found to be similar.	✓	
b) Different animals may have evolved from the same ancestor.		✓
c) Natural selection is the process by which evolution takes place.		✓
d) DNA from related animals shows a lot of similarity.	✓	

Q3   The statements below are observations of life on Earth. **Circle** the statements that the theory of natural selection **accounts for**, and **underline** those that **conflict** with it.

> Species of finch on the Galapagos islands have different shaped beaks that suit their preferred food.

> Some species features cannot be explained by a series of smaller changes that are all advantageous.

> The fossil record shows a series of large changes — not a sequence of small changes.

> The variety of peppered moth with dark wings became more common after the industrial revolution.

Q4   Darwin's observations conflicted with the **accepted idea** about the development of species.

a)   Suggest why scientists were **reluctant** to give up the accepted idea for the development of species.

...*religion*...

b)   Suggest why most scientists now accept natural selection as the **best explanation** for evolution.

....

c)   Suggest a reason why some scientists still **disagree** with the theory of natural selection.

....

Human Evolution

Q1   The **brain** is a very important part of the human body.

a)   How does the size of the human brain in relation to body size compare with other species?

....

b)   Suggest two ways that ancient humans were given
a **survival advantage** by the size of their brains?

1. ....

2. ....

Q2   The diagram below shows how **modern humans** evolved from **early man**.

a)   Circle all the species that exist **today**.

b)   What has happened to the other species?

....

c)   **i)**   Which of the species below would you expect modern
humans to be most similar to?
Circle the correct answer.

Homo habilis   **Homo heidelbergensis**

ii)   Give a reason for your answer.

....

iii) Why do all three species in part i) share some characteristics?

....

Q3   In 1912, scientists discovered bones which appeared to be from an early human. However the evidence from these bones **conflicted** with the **accepted idea** of human evolution.

a)   Give two reasons why a piece of evidence might conflict with an established theory.

1. ....

2. ....

b)   What effect would the discovery of **conflicting evidence** have on people's confidence in a theory?

....

c)   Most of the evidence currently available supports the theory of human evolution shown in
question 2. Is this **proof** that the theory is true? Give a reason for your answer.

....

Module B3 — Life On Earth

The Nervous System

Q1 Tick the boxes to indicate whether the following statements are **true** or **false**.

True   False

a) As multicellular organisms got bigger they became less complicated. ☐ ☐

b) Different parts of complex organisms are specialised for different jobs. ☐ ☐

c) Multicellular organisms evolved nervous and hormonal systems to
coordinate and communicate between different parts of their bodies. ☐ ☐

d) The nervous system is used for slow, long-lasting responses. ☐ ☐

Q2 Complete the following passage about the nervous system by choosing the correct words.

electrical impulses   brain   stimuli   receptors   effectors   sense   heart   spinal cord

The body has .... organs which detect ....

These organs contain ...., which send signals along nerve

cells (neurones) to the .... or .... using

....

Q3 The nervous system is made up of several different parts.

a) Draw arrows between the boxes in the diagram to show the flow of information from a stimulus
through the nervous system to the response.

CNS

Receptor   Effector

Stimulus   Response

Motor   Sensory
neurone   neurone

b) Outline the function of the following parts of the nervous system:

i) Receptor cells ....

ii) Sensory neurones ....

iii) CNS ....

iv) Motor neurones ....

v) Effector cells ....

c) The sensory system is driven by stimuli. What is a stimulus?

....

The Nervous System

Q4 Complete the table with the entries given to show the **sense organs** and the type of **receptors** they contain.

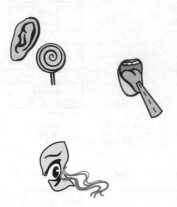

Organ	Receptor type
	Light
Nose	
	Sound / balance
Tongue	
	Touch / temperature

Ear

Taste

Skin

Smell

Eye

Q5 The nervous system allows you to react to a **stimulus**.

a) What are the two parts of the central nervous system called?

....

b) Which of the following statements best describes nervous responses? Circle the correct answer.

Fast and long-lasting   Slow and long-lasting   Fast and short-lived   Slow and short-lived

c) i) What are the two types of effector in the human body?

....

ii) How does each of these effectors respond to an instruction from the CNS?

1. ....

2. ....

Q6 Susie has been given a **box of sweets** for her birthday. She decides she would like to eat a **red** one.

Explain how her nervous system allows her to:

i) Find the red sweet. ....

....

ii) Pick it up to eat. ....

....

Top Tips: There's no need to be nervous about questions on the nervous system — just remember how all the bits work together and it'll be a piece of cake. That's a victoria sponge cake with jam and cream in the middle in case you were wondering — ooh and a nice cup of tea too.

Hormones

Q1 Complete the following passage by choosing the correct words from those given.

blood   fast   long   target   short   chemicals   air   slow   glands   impulses   nerve

Hormones are .... which are made in .... and released into the .... They are carried around the body until they reach a .... cell where they act. Hormones are generally quite .... to act, but their effects last a .... time.

Q2 Tick the boxes to show whether the following responses are mainly controlled by the **nervous** or **hormonal** systems.

	Nervous system	Hormonal system
a) Hearing the alarm clock and turning it off.	☐	☐
b) Your heart beating faster when you remember you have an exam that day.	☐	☐
c) Smelling toast burning.	☐	☐
d) Your hairs standing on end when you're cold.	☐	☐

Q3 Rob is watching a horror film when some tense music starts. His **pupils dilate** and a few seconds later his **heart** starts **beating faster**. The tension passes and Rob's pupils return to normal immediately, but his heart takes a few minutes to slow down.

a) Describe how Rob's **hormonal system** controlled one of his responses to the scary film.

....

b) Describe how Rob's **nervous system** controlled his other response.

....

Q4 **Homeostasis** is important for keeping the body working properly.

a) What does homeostasis mean?

....

b) Name two body systems involved in homeostasis.

....

c) Describe how the body controls blood sugar levels after a meal.

....

....

Module B3 — Life On Earth

Interdependence

Q1   The resources below are **essential** for life.

a)   Draw lines to connect the boxes to show which resources are essential for plants, essential for animals and essential for both.

Light   Plants   Oxygen

Carbon Dioxide   Water

Minerals   Animals   Food

b)   What would happen if an essential resource was in short supply?

....

c)   Give one way that organisms are dependent on other species for their survival.

....

Q2   The following table shows the number of **rabbits** in a certain area over the last **five years**.

Year	2001	2002	2003	2004	2005
Number of rabbits	103	128	118	109	67

a)   Calculate the mean number of rabbits in this area over the last 5 years.

....

b)   In which year was the number of rabbits significantly lower than average?

....

c)   Suggest two reasons for the decreased rabbit population in this year.

1. ....

2. ....

Q3   **Rapid environmental change** can cause a species to become **extinct**.
Suggest **three** changes which could cause the extinction of a species.

1. ....

2. ....

3. ....

Interdependence

Q4 The diagram below shows a **woodland food web**. Last year a chemical was spilt in the woods, and turned out to be poisonous to voles. The population of **voles** significantly **decreased**.

a) Suggest an explanation for each of the following consequences:

i) The population of barn owls **decreasing**.

....

ii) The population of insects **increasing**.

....

iii) The population of insects **decreasing**.

....

b) Suggest what might happen to the **bird population**. Give a reason for your answer.

....

....

Q5 The diagram shows part of a food web from Nebraska in the USA. The **flowerhead weevil** doesn't occur naturally in this area. It was introduced by **farmers** to eat the musk thistle which is a weed.

a) Why might the introduction of the flowerhead weevil decrease the number of platte thistles?

....

b) What effect will this have on the amount of wild honey produced in the area? Give a reason for your answer.

....

....

....

c) Suggest a reason why the population of platte thistles may increase as the population of musk thistles is reduced by the introduction of flowerhead weevils.

....

....

Top Tips: Interdependence is just like happy families — dad relies on mum, the kids rely on mum and dad, mum relies on Auntie Nora... Families don't tend to eat each other though, so it's not quite the same — my sister looks like she wants to eat me sometimes, but I don't think she will.

Humans and the Earth

Q1 Tick the boxes to indicate whether the following statements are **true** or **false**.

		True	False
a)	A species is said to be extinct when there are no more individuals of that species.	☐	☐
b)	A lot of extinctions have been caused by human activity.	☐	☐
c)	Sustainable development requires that some species are made extinct.	☐	☐
d)	Humans may cause extinction directly by irresponsibly managing habitats.	☐	☐

Q2 **Human activity** can contribute to the **extinction** of animals.

a) Give an example to show how each of the following human actions have caused species to become extinct.

   i) Hunting ....

   ....

   ii) Introduction of a new species to a habitat ....

   ....

   iii) Destruction of a habitat ....

   ....

   iv) Killing of a species to protect livestock ....

   ....

b) Which of the actions given in part a) describe an extinction **directly** caused by humans? Circle the correct answer(s).

      i)   **ii)**   **iii)**   **iv)**

Q3 Maintaining the Earth's **biodiversity** is very important.

a) What does 'biodiversity' mean?

   ....

b) Suggest how the Earth's biodiversity can be maintained.

   ....

c) Give three reasons why maintaining biodiversity is important.

   1. ....

   2. ....

   3. ....

Recycling Elements

Q1 Use these words to complete the blanks.

> feeding   soil   excrete   microbes   cycling   decompose   leaves   roots

There is a continual .... of elements on Earth. In plants, elements are taken

in through the .... and .... Animals take in elements

through .... and respiration. Elements are returned to the environment

when animals .... or when animals and plants die and

.... This process of decay is carried out by ...., such

as bacteria. The elements released by decay either enter the .... or go into

the air, where they can be taken up again by other living organisms.

Q2 Plants take in **elements** and **compounds** from the environment.

a) Give three elements that are constantly recycled through living organisms.

....

b) Describe how an element present in the **soil** can become part of an animal.

....

....

c) Name one type of molecule that plants use **nitrates** to make.

....

Q3 Circle the correct word(s) to complete the sentences below.

a) Nitrogen gas in the atmosphere is turned into nitrates by **nitrifying** / **nitrogen-fixing** bacteria.

b) Bacteria that convert organic waste, such as rotting plants, into ammonium compounds are called **nitrogen-fixing bacteria** / **decomposers**.

c) Ammonium compounds are turned into useful nitrates by **nitrifying** / **nitrogen-fixing** bacteria.

d) Nitrates in the soil are turned back into nitrogen gas in the air by **denitrifying bacteria** / **decomposers**.

Q4 Bacteria can turn nitrogen in the air into **nitrates** in the soil.

Name another way that nitrogen in the air can be turned into nitrates in the soil.

....

Organic and Intensive Farming

Q1 Elements are lost from the soil when crops are harvested.

a) Name three important chemical elements that are lost from the soil.

....

b) What happens to the fertility of the soil if these elements are not replaced? ....

c) Use the words given below to complete the passage.

fertile   cycle   sewage   manure   crop rotation

Organic farmers keep their fields .... by replacing lost elements

in the soil. For example, they spread ...., compost or human

.... on the land. They also use ...., which

means that they grow a different crop each year in a ....

d) Organic farmers may grow 'green manure'. Explain what this means.

....

e) How do intensive farmers replace elements lost from the soil?

....

Q2 Tick the boxes to show whether the statements are **true** or **false**.   True False

a) Pests and disease can greatly reduce crop yields.

b) Ladybirds are pests that can affect crops.

c) Potato blight is a disease that can kill crop plants.

d) Crop rotation can be used to control pests and disease.

e) Intensive farming is regulated by the Soil Association.

Q3 Choose from the words below to complete the passage.

control   resist   biological processes   wide   crop rotation   pesticides   predators   narrow

Organic farmers can use .... to deal with pests and

disease. For example, they can use natural .... to biologically

.... pests such as greenfly. .... helps to prevent the pests

and diseases of one particular crop building up in an area. Varieties of plants can be grown that

are best able to .... pests and diseases. .... field edges

can be left uncultivated to encourage larger insects and other animals that feed on pests.

Organic and Intensive Farming

Q4 A farmer grows a crop of maize in a field for six consecutive years. The **yield** of maize each year is recorded in the bar chart.

a) Describe the trend shown by the data, and suggest a reason for it.

....

....

b) One year's yield doesn't fit the trend. Which year is it? Suggest a reason for this result.

....

c) Give one organic and one intensive method the farmer could use to improve his crop yields.

....

....

Q5 Intensive farming relies on **artificial fertilisers**.

a) Give three advantages of using artificial fertilisers rather than organic methods.

....

....

b) When artificial fertilisers are washed into rivers, they can cause eutrophication. Describe what happens in eutrophication and why it's a problem.

....

....

c) Explain why an organic farmer may choose to grow peas in a field the year before he grows cabbages there.

....

Q6 Intensive farmers use **man-made** chemical pesticides.

a) Give two advantages of using man-made chemical pesticides to treat crops.

....

....

b) How could pesticide spraying cause harm to humans who consume the crop?

....

c) What effect might chemical pesticides have on ecosystems in or near to the crops being sprayed?

....

<u>*Organic and Intensive Farming*</u>

Q7 Sameer and Philippa compare the prices of chicken in a supermarket. An **organic** chicken costs £8.99, a **non-organic free-range** chicken costs £6.99, while a **non-organic** chicken raised by **intensive battery farming** costs £3.99. All three are the same size.

a) Suggest three reasons why there is a difference in price.

Think about animal welfare, growth promotion, and feeding costs.

....

....

....

....

....

Q8 A company tested a new fertiliser, **Fert X**, to see whether it produced a better crop yield than their existing fertiliser, **OldFert**. A field was divided into two equal areas and cabbages were planted in both. In area A, 50 kg of Fert X was applied, and in area B 50 kg of OldFert was applied. After three months, the cabbages were harvested and the mass of cabbages produced from each area recorded. Area A produced a **higher yield** of cabbages than area B.

a) Give three controlled variables in this experiment.

....

....

b) Suggest two reasons why this experiment might not have been a fair test.

....

....

c) The company decides not to produce and sell Fert X. Suggest two reasons, one economic and one environmental, why they may have made this decision.

....

....

d) The company draws the conclusion that 'Both Fert X and OldFert are effective fertilisers for cabbages.' Are they right to say this based on the trial above? If not, what further experiment would they need to do?

....

....

Natural Polymers

Q1 Polymers are formed from the combination of lots of smaller molecules known as **monomers**.

Name two groups of compounds that are natural polymers.

....

Q2 Carbohydrates can be monomers or polymers.

a) Circle the elements below that are found in **carbohydrates**.

nitrogen   carbon   oxygen   sulfur   sodium   hydrogen   gold

b) Name a carbohydrate monomer. ....

c) Match up the complex carbohydrate polymer with its function.

cellulose   energy storage in plants

glycogen   structural material in plants

starch   energy storage in animals

Q3 Label the monomers in these diagrams.

a) .... protein

b) .... starch

Q4 Tick the boxes to show whether the statements are **true** or **false**.

True False

a) Amino acids join together to form proteins. ☐ ☐

b) Proteins contain the elements carbon, hydrogen, oxygen and nitrogen. ☐ ☐

c) There are about 200 different amino acids. ☐ ☐

d) Plants take in nitrates from the soil and react them with carbon dioxide to make amino acids. ☐ ☐

e) Amino acids are polymers. ☐ ☐

Module C3 — Food Matters

Digestion

Q1 Circle the correct words to complete the sentences below.

a) Food is made up of **small** / **big** molecules such as starch, proteins, and fats.

b) Digestion is the process of **breaking down** / **building up** large molecules.

c) Small molecules that are **soluble** / **insoluble** can enter the blood.

d) Glucose and amino acids enter the blood in the **small** / **large** intestine.

Q2 Match up the foods with the polymers they contain, and the monomers they're made up of.

bread / potatoes / muesli

starch

amino acids

meat / eggs / fish

proteins

glucose molecules

Q3 There are an enormous number of different **proteins** in the human body, yet there are only a small number of different **amino acids**.

a) Explain how amino acids are able to form this huge variety of proteins.

....

b) Give four parts of the body that are mainly made of proteins.

....

Q4 Use the words below to fill in the blanks in the passage.

urine	liver	blood	excreted	urea
proteins		excess	kidneys	growing

Amino acids are transported around the body in the .... They are

taken up by .... cells which need them to make ....

Any amino acids that cannot be used at once have to be .... These

.... amino acids are taken to the .... where they are

converted into .... This is taken by the blood to the ..../

where it is passed out in the ....

Insulin and Diabetes

Q1 Diabetes is a disorder involving the hormone **insulin**.

a) Which organ in the human body produces insulin? ....

b) How does insulin help to control blood sugar levels?

....

c) In which organ is excess sugar converted into glycogen? ....

d) What happens if there's too much sugar for it all to be stored as glycogen?

....

e) Circle the correct words to complete the paragraph below.

> When you eat foods that contain a lot of sugar, the sugar enters your
> bloodstream **slowly / quickly**, making your blood sugar level **rise / fall** very
> quickly. Instead of sugary foods, dietitians recommend that you should eat
> foods that contain complex **carbohydrates / proteins** like **rice / chocolate**,
> which are gradually broken down into **fat / sugar** by the body.

Q2 Nigel is a trainee doctor. As part of his training he is presented with case studies of two patients.

Patient X is 50 years old. She has visited the doctor to complain of increasing tiredness, constant thirst and a frequent need to 'visit the toilet for a wee'. On questioning, she admits to a poor diet, based on processed foods and sugar-rich soft drinks, and she is overweight. A urine test and a blood test show that she has abnormally high blood glucose levels.

Patient Y is 6 years old. She has been taken to hospital suffering from nausea and vomiting. Her symptoms have developed suddenly. She is severely dehydrated and close to falling into a coma. A blood test shows that she has abnormally high glucose levels. Patient Y's parents state that prior to this emergency, she had seemed a healthy child.

a) **i)** Which patient may have type 1 diabetes? ....

ii) Explain your answer. ....

....

b) What advice on lifestyle should the doctor give Patient X?

....

Top Tips: Normally, insulin (which lowers blood sugar levels) is produced in response to an increase in blood sugar level. Diabetics can't control their blood sugar levels properly using insulin, so it's really important for them to control their diet — to try and keep their sugar levels stable.

Module C3 — Food Matters

Insulin and Diabetes

Q3 Choose from the words below to complete the passages about diabetes.

pancreas   diet   death   weekly   weight   sugar   enough
insulin   younger   responding   daily   high   brain   older

a) Type 1 diabetes usually develops in .... people, when the

.... stops producing .... Blood

.... levels can become so .... that they

damage the body, possibly causing coma and .... This type

of diabetes can be controlled with .... injections of insulin.

b) Type 2 diabetes usually affects .... people. It develops either

because the body stops making .... insulin or because the

body stops .... to it normally. Type 2 diabetes is controlled by

improving the ...., losing .... and exercising.

Q4 Why is type 2 diabetes becoming more common in young people?

....

....

Q5 Thelma finishes eating a meal at 12 o'clock, and her blood sugar (glucose) levels are monitored for the next three hours. The results are shown on the graph.

Blood glucose level (mg/100 cm³)

a) What is the normal blood glucose level in Thelma's blood?

....

b) By how much does her blood glucose rise after the meal?

....

c) How long does it take after finishing the meal for Thelma's blood glucose level to return to normal?

....

d) Thelma's pancreas works normally at the moment. If Thelma developed diabetes and her body stopped producing enough insulin, predict two differences that you might notice on the graph for a similar experiment.

....

....

Harmful Chemicals in Food

Q1 Draw lines to match the foods with the dangers associated with them.

uncooked cassava

rashes, swellings, vomiting, diarrhoea and breathing problems

proteins in peanuts

cyanide poisoning

gluten in wheat

rash and swelling of the mouth and throat

Q2 In farming, both **pesticides** and **herbicides** are widely used. Pesticides are used to kill insects and other pest organisms.

a) Why might residues of pesticides and herbicides be found in the food we eat?

....

b) Many parents now feed their babies with organic baby food. Suggest why they might have taken this precaution.

....

....

Q3 Some foods can produce **aflatoxin** if they are not stored properly.

a) Give two examples of foods that can produce aflatoxin if stored incorrectly.

....

b) What produces the aflatoxin in these foods?

....

c) Give one health problem that can be caused by eating food containing aflatoxin.

....

d) Explain why it may be dangerous for humans to eat food produced for animals, such as bird seed.

....

Top Tips: It's important to remember that just because something is eaten very commonly, it's not necessarily completely safe. Some foods are naturally dangerous. Some contain potentially harmful chemicals from farming. Others develop dangerous chemicals during storage or cooking.

Module C3 — Food Matters

Harmful Chemicals in Food

Q4 Harmful chemicals can be formed when **cooking** foods.

a) Name two harmful chemicals that can be produced when food is cooked at high temperatures.

....

b) How do these chemicals cause cancer when consumed by animals?

....

c) Give three ways of reducing the amounts of these harmful chemicals in your diet.

....

....

d) It is known that grilling meat at high temperatures produces harmful chemicals. Why do many people still cook meat this way? Give three reasons.

....

....

....

Q5 Potatoes produce a toxic chemical called **solanine**, which is present in high levels in the potato plant's leaves and shoots. The potato itself has a relatively low level of solanine, but this level can rise if it is not stored properly. **Green** potatoes are an indicator of high levels of solanine. Solanine concentrates especially in the **potato skin**, and cannot be removed by washing or cooking.

For an average person, a lethal dose of solanine can be about 5 milligrams per kilogram of body mass. Even correctly stored potatoes can contain about 200 milligrams per kilogram.

a) Calculate the dose of solanine that would be lethal for a 50 kg person.

....

b) What mass of potatoes would need to be eaten to produce this lethal dose?

....

c) Suggest how to prepare potatoes in order to reduce the amounts of solanine eaten.

....

d) Give two reasons why potatoes aren't banned by the Government or the European Union, even though they contain such high levels of dangerous chemicals.

....

....

Food Additives

Q1 Lots of foods contain additives.

a) Why are **food colours** added to some foods? ....

b) What is the difference between **flavourings** and **flavour enhancers**?

....

....

c) Why are diet drinks made with artificial sweeteners?

....

Q2 Choose from these words to complete the blanks.

foul-smelling   sodium benzoate   antioxidants
oxygen   rancid   preservatives   nitrogen

Foods that contain fats or oils can go off by reacting with ....

in the air.   Butter can go .... as the oxygen breaks down the

fat into .... products. To prevent this from happening,

chemicals called .... are added to food containing fats or oils.

Other foods can have ...., such as ....,

added to prevent the growth of harmful microbes.

Maths homework...
— food additives.

Q3 **Emulsifiers** and **stabilisers** can be added to certain foods.

a) Why are emulsifiers necessary in some foods?

....

b) What are stabilisers used in foods for?

....

Q4 Some food additives are thought to cause health problems.

a) If a food additive has been given an **E number**, what does this mean?

....

b) Why might a food additive with an E number **not** be allowed to be used in the USA or Canada?

....

c) Give three health problems linked to food additives.

....

....

Module C3 — Food Matters

Keeping Food Safe

Q1   Read the information below and then answer the questions that follow.

Bovine spongiform encephalopathy (BSE) is a cattle disease that first appeared in Britain in the mid-1980s. It leads to a fatal degeneration of brain function. The early symptoms of disorientation and shakiness caused it to be popularly termed 'mad cow disease'.

A probable link between BSE and a newly discovered fatal brain disease in humans, variant Creutzfeldt-Jakob Disease (vCJD), was found, leading to an international crisis about the safety of British beef for human consumption.

This timeline shows how the problem developed:

 December 1984 — A cow on a farm in Sussex becomes the first confirmed victim of BSE, dying early in 1985. Other cows begin to show the same symptoms.

 November 1986 — BSE becomes recognised as a new cattle disease.

 October 1987 — BSE is found to be similar to the existing disease, scrapie, in sheep. Scientists begin suggesting that BSE may be caused by feeding cattle with protein derived from the carcasses of other animals, such as sheep.

July 1988 — Many animal proteins are banned from sheep and cattle feed.

 February 1989 — An expert scientific committee, the Spongiform Encephalopathy Advisory Committee (SEAC), is established.

 November 1989 — Certain forms of bovine offal, such as brains and spleens, are banned from human foods.

 May 1990 — A pet cat is found to have a BSE-like disease. This is the first indication (outside a lab) that BSE might be able to infect a different species.

 1992/1993 — BSE reaches a peak, affecting 0.3% of Britain's cattle.

 May 1995 — The first person dies from vCJD.

 March 1996 — SEAC announces a probable link between BSE in cattle and vCJD in humans. News reports give predictions of human deaths in the UK from vCJD that range from hundreds to tens of thousands.

 March 1996 — The EU (European Union) bans British beef exports.

 August 1996 — Cattle most at risk from BSE are slaughtered.

 February 2003 — Predicted deaths from vCJD are now thought to be at worst 7000.

 December 2004 — Total number of people in Britain with vCJD reaches 150.

Module C3 — Food Matters

Keeping Food Safe

a) Tick the boxes to show whether the following sentences are **data** or **explanations**.

Data   Explanation

i) The pet cat had a disease similar to BSE. ☐ ☐

ii) BSE was able to jump the species barrier and infect a pet cat. ☐ ☐

b) Give two measures that were taken to prevent the spread of BSE.

....

....

c) **i)** Using ideas about **feasibility**, **risk** and **benefit**, suggest why the British Government never decided to completely ban beef for human consumption.

....

....

....

ii) What is likely to have caused the EU to ban British beef exports in 1996?

....

d) In 1992/1993 there were about 12 000 000 cattle in the UK. Approximately how many were affected by BSE?

....

e) The first person died from vCJD relatively late into the BSE crisis. Suggest why scientists couldn't accurately predict, in 1996, how many people would die from vCJD.

....

....

f) In December 2003, a British man died from vCJD, which he was thought to have developed following a blood transfusion seven years earlier. Many countries took action to ban people who had lived in Britain during the BSE crisis from being **blood donors**.

i) Use the idea of the '**precautionary principle**' to explain why some countries took that action.

....

....

ii) Suggest why the UK Blood Service did not implement a similar ban.

....

....

Module C3 — Food Matters

Eating Healthily

Q1   Read the following newspaper article and then answer the questions that follow.

'Fish Oil Supplements Boost Exam Performance'   August 2005

It has been long established in folk wisdom that a healthy body leads to a healthy mind. One school in Sheepshire has put this claim to the test by giving all its Year 11 students daily fish oil supplements in the year running up to their GCSEs.

Thomasina Gradgrind, headteacher of Thwackum School, said that the improvements have been remarkable. "In 2004, 40% of our candidates achieved at least five A*-C grades at GCSE. But this year, following the use of the fish oil supplements, we have seen this boosted to 50%."

There has been huge media interest in the school's project and many of the students have featured in local and national newspapers. One student, Kyle, was the subject of a documentary on national TV. "It was amazing," he said. "I used to hate school and often played truant. But this year, I settled down and studied hard for my exams. I'm really pleased with my results, and I'm hoping to begin a training course at college in September."

The fish oil capsules given to the students are rich in omega-3 fatty acids, which scientists believe to be essential for brain function. These fatty acids are found in oily fish such as sardines and mackerel but are often lacking in the diet of many people.

However, a leading scientist in the study of how diet affects behaviour, Professor Carlos Carlosson of Ox-fridge University, expressed doubts about the results. "I was disappointed to see that there was no proper control, and that the use of 'dummy' pills had not been included in the study. Besides, the media attention may have biased the results."

Ms Gradgrind dismisses the criticism and remains convinced of the positive effects of fish oil pills. "I would like to thank all my students and staff. Everyone has made a special effort this year, and the results are terrific!"

---

a)   Use the information in the article, and your knowledge of scientific ideas, to consider whether the following statements are **true**, **false**, or you **can't say**.

	True	False	Can't say
i) The GCSE results improved at Thwackum School from 2004 to 2005.	☐	☐	☐
ii) Fish oil supplements improve exam performance.	☐	☐	☐
iii) Some students at Thwackum School took 'dummy' pills during the study.	☐	☐	☐
iv) Key Stage 3 students given fish oil supplements will get better results, on average, in their SATs.	☐	☐	☐
v) Further studies are needed to give greater confidence in the connection between fish oil supplements and exam performance.	☐	☐	☐

b)   One of Professor Carlosson's concerns is that Thwackum School doesn't have many students in each year group compared to many other schools.
Why might he be concerned about the number of students involved in this study?

....

Eating Healthily

c) A new homework club and Saturday tuition for GCSE Maths, English and Science were introduced at the same time as the fish oil pills. Why is this a flaw in the design of the experiment?

....

....

d) Professor Carlosson is concerned that **media attention** may have biased the study.
How might this attention have influenced the behaviour of the students, parents and teachers?

Students: ....

Parents: ....

Teachers: ....

e) Professor Carlosson thinks that while fish oil pills are an excellent source of omega-3 fatty acids, it is better for people to get their omega-3 fatty acids from a healthy balanced diet.
Suggest why this might be the case.

....

....

f) Professor Carlosson conducts a new study into the influence of fish oil supplements on GCSE exam performance. He selects at random 50% of the students to take **fish oil supplements** during Year 11. The other 50% of students are given **'dummy'** pills. No student is told which type of pill they are being given. Their GCSE Maths results are shown in the graph.

i) How many students in total were involved in this study?

....

....

ii) Calculate the percentage of students obtaining grades A*-C in each group.

Students taking fish oil pills: ....

....

Students taking 'dummy' pills: ....

....

iii) Despite the higher number of students taking the fish oil supplements obtaining grades A*-C, Professor Carlosson doesn't think these results provide evidence that fish oils improve Maths performance. Other than fish oils, suggest an explanation for this higher number.

....

....

Module P3 — Radioactive Materials

Radioactivity

Q1 Label this diagram of an **atom** with the words in blue.

nucleus   protons   neutrons   electrons

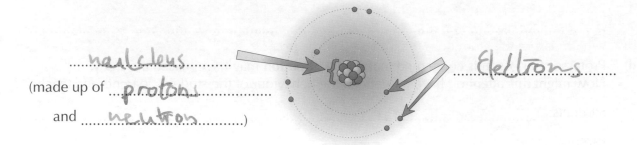

.......naulcleus........   Elelltrons........

(made up of .....protons.............

and ......neltron........)

Q2 Draw lines to connect the beginning of each sentence with its ending.

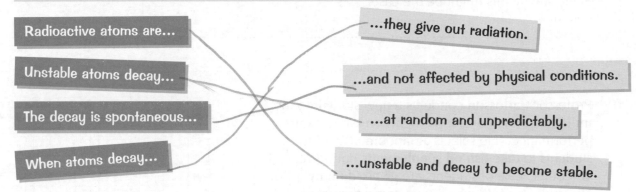

Radioactive atoms are...

Unstable atoms decay...

The decay is spontaneous...

When atoms decay...

...they give out radiation.

...and not affected by physical conditions.

...at random and unpredictably.

...unstable and decay to become stable.

Q3 **Chlorine** has two stable isotopes. Each has **17 protons** in its nucleus.

a) What will be different about the nuclei of these two isotopes?

They will contain different number of Nestrons

b) Define the term 'isotopes'?

An isotope that is not radioactive

c) What is meant by a **stable isotope**?

An Atoms withs the same nummeber of protons but a different number of neutrons

Q4 Underline the **factor(s)** that can affect the amount of **radiation** emitted by a radioactive source.

The ambient temperature   The shape of the sample

How much of the substance there is

The Three Kinds of Nuclear Radiation

Q1 There are three types of **nuclear radiation**.

a) What are these three types?

alpha, beta, gamma

b) Which part of the atom does the radiation come from?

Nucleus

c) Which type of radiation is not a particle?

Gamma - It's part of the Em spectrum

DANGER
HARMFUL
REVISION
DO NOT READ

Q2 The ability of radiation to **penetrate** a material depends on what **kind** of radiation it is.

a) Which type(s) of radiation could escape from a **paper bag**?

beta and gamma

b) Which type(s) of radiation will pass through a thin sheet of **aluminium**?

gamma

c) Which type of radiation can only be stopped by a thick **lead sheet** or very thick **concrete**?

gamma

Q3 Choose from the words given below to complete the paragraph.
You may have to use a word more than once, or not at all.

electrons   three   big   two   slowly   easily
light   element   heavy   neutrons   penetrate   protons

Alpha particles are relatively *big* and
heavy and move fairly *slowly*. They are
stopped *easily* and don't *penetrate* far into
materials. Alpha particles come from very *big*
nuclei, and are made of two *protons* and
two neutrons. When an atom releases an alpha
particle the atom changes into a different *element*
because it has two fewer *proton*.

The Three Kinds of Nuclear Radiation

Q4   **Uranium-238** decays by giving off an **alpha particle**, as shown by this nuclear equation:

$$^{238}_{92}U \longrightarrow X + ^4_2\alpha$$

a)   Calculate the mass number and atomic number of X.

    i)   The atomic number of X is .... 90 ....

    ii)   The mass number of X is ...... 234 ....

b)   Use a periodic table to identify X. .... Thorium ....

Q5   Connect the two parts of these sentences by drawing lines between them.

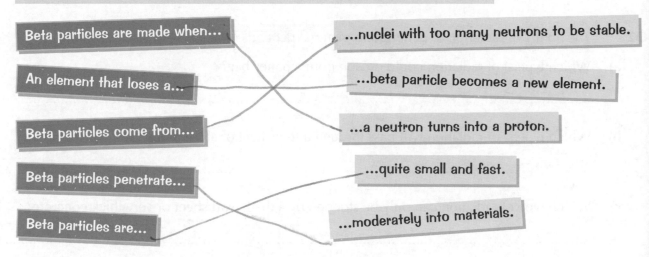

Beta particles are made when...

An element that loses a...

Beta particles come from...

Beta particles penetrate...

Beta particles are...

...nuclei with too many neutrons to be stable.

...beta particle becomes a new element.

...a neutron turns into a proton.

...quite small and fast.

...moderately into materials.

Q6   Answer the following questions on **gamma radiation**.

a)   Give two ways in which gamma radiation is completely different from alpha and beta radiation.

    1. ... Gamma radiation is in the electromagnetic spectrum

    2. ... Gamma rays have no mass ....

b)   In what circumstances would a nucleus emit gamma radiation?

... nothing needs to loss some excess energy .

c)   Why is a gamma source difficult to store safely?

... gamma radiation can be used to penetrate most materials ...

d)   When alpha and beta radiation are emitted, new elements are formed.
Explain why this doesn't happen with gamma radiation.

... Gamma rays are just energy ....

Half-Life

Q1   Tick the boxes to show whether the following statements are **true** or **false**.

True False

a)   The number of radioactive nuclei in a sample always stays the same.   ☐ ☑

b)   Radioactive materials decay at different rates.   ☑ ☐

Q2   Complete the following sentences using some of the words given below.

| short   quickly   decay   half   long   melt   slowly   all |

a)   The half-life of a sample is the time taken for ..._half_........ of the radioactive

atoms present to ..._decay_.........

b)   A long half-life means that the activity falls ...._slowly_......

c)   A short half-life means that the activity falls ...._quicker_..... because a lot

of the nuclei decay in a ...._short_........ time.

_Dave regretted performing
a DIY X-ray on himself._

Q3   The half-life of strontium-90 is **29 years**.

a)   What does this tell you will have happened to a pure sample of strontium-90 in 29 years' time?

...._half life atoms will have decayed_........

b)   If you start with 1000 atoms of strontium-90, how many
would you expect there to be left after 87 years?

...._125_........

Q4   The activity of a radioactive sample is **1440 cpm**. 5 hours later
it has fallen to **45 cpm**. What is the half-life of this material?

...._1 half life = 1 hour_........

Q5   The half-life of a radioactive material is **5400 years**.

a)   If its activity now is **24 cpm**, how long will it take to drop to **3 cpm**?

...._24 ÷ 12 ÷ 2, 12 ÷ 2 = 6. 6 ÷ 2 = 3. 3 half lives. 3 × 5400 × 16200_........

b)   How long ago was the sample's activity **96 cpm**?

...._10' 800 years_........

Danger from Nuclear Radiation

Q1 Complete the paragraph below using the words in blue.

cells	cancer	ions	radiation sickness	kill	break	ionising

Alpha, beta and gamma radiation can be described as ......*ionising*...... radiation because when they hit molecules they ......*break*...... them into bits called ......*ions*......

A high dose of radiation will ......*kill*...... cells causing ......*radiation sickness*......

whereas smaller doses damage cells, which can cause ......*cancer*......

Q2 We can be affected by radiation in two ways — **contamination** and **irradiation**.

a) Explain the difference between contamination and irradiation.

......*radiation doesn't involve contact with the source.*......
......*Contamination involves some of the source being attached.*......

b) Give **two** examples of situations where you could be...

i) irradiated

1. ......*mining*......
2. ......*performing an x-ray*......

ii) contaminated

1. ......*picking up a radioactive sample*......
2. ......*eating something with radioactive dust*......

Q3 The **amount** of radiation people receive varies depending on their **profession**.

a) Give 3 groups of people who are at a higher risk from radiation than average.

1. ......*radiographers*......   2. ......*uranium*......

3. ......*miners*......

b) For each of your 3 groups, explain where the extra radiation comes from.

1. ......
2. ......
3. ......

Q4 Explain why ionising radiation can cause **damage** to parts of the body that weren't **directly** irradiated.

Think about ions in the body...

......

Module P3 — Radioactive Materials

Danger from Nuclear Radiation

Q5 Radiation doses are measured in Sieverts (Sv).

a) While you are reading this you are receiving about 2 mSv/year. What is causing this?

background radiation

b) The table below shows some typical radiation doses.

	Dose in Sv
Dose required to sterilise medical products	25 000 (single dose)
Typical total radiotherapy dose to cancer tumour	60
50% survival probability, whole body dose	4 (single dose)
Legal worker dose limit (whole body)	0.02 per year
Average dose from all sources in Cornwall	0.008 per year
Average dose from natural radiation	0.002 per year
Typical chest X-ray dose	0.00002 (single dose)
Average dose from a UK to Spain flight	0.00001 (single dose)

i) Suggest why people living in Cornwall have a higher than normal dose.

the type of rocks underground

ii) Why is the high dose used in cancer treatment not fatal? *Think about what gets irradiated...*

Radiation is focused on 1 spot

iii) How many chest X-rays would the average person need in one year in order to double their radiation dose?

0.002 ÷ 0.00002 = 100

iv) A British pilot flies to Spain **and back** 500 times per year. If he lives in Cornwall, is his annual dose below the legal worker limit?

Yes. (1000 × 0.00001) + 0.008 = 0.018

Top Tips: Annual radiation doses can vary a fair bit from person to person. Everyone's exposed to a low level of **background radiation** every day, though — from rocks etc. — and you can't do anything about that (unless you fancy wearing a lead-lined suit and breathing apparatus all day long).

Module P3 — Radioactive Materials

2116

Using Nuclear Radiation

Q1 For a radioactive material to be considered 'safe', its activity should be at or below the normal **background level**.

a) A sample of cobalt-60 has an activity of **24 Bq**. The background count is **6 Bq**. The half-life of cobalt-60 is **5 years**. How long will it take for the sample to reach a 'safe' level of activity?

24÷2=12 . 12÷2=6 . So: two half lives

b) What would be the safest material to **store** the sample in until it is 'safe'? thick lead

Q2 **Gamma rays** can damage cells and cause cancer. They are also used to treat cancer by **radiotherapy**. A **narrow beam** of gamma rays is **focused** onto the cancer cells and kills them.

a) Explain why it's important in radiotherapy to use a **narrow** beam of gamma rays and to **focus** it carefully.

b) Why do patients often feel very ill after radiotherapy?

Q3 Match up the beginnings and endings of the sentences below.

Background radiation is...

Naturally radioactive materials...

Cosmic rays are...

Cosmic rays...

...come mainly from the Sun.

...a source of background radiation.

...radiation that is all around us.

...include soil, rocks and the air.

Q4 **Surgical instruments** used to be made of metal and were sterilised by **boiling**. Now, many are made of plastics.

a) Many plastic instruments can't be sterilised by boiling. Explain why.

b) Instruments are often sterilised **after** they have been sealed in plastic bags. Why is irradiation of the instruments still possible?

c) The gamma source used to irradiate instruments normally has a long half-life. Why is this?

d) Name something else that gamma rays are often used to sterilise.

Module P3 — Radioactive Materials

Radiation and Risk

Q1   Read the passage below and answer the questions that follow.

Cornish homeowners at risk from radiation

A scientific study has taken place which charted the levels of the radioactive gas, radon, across England and Wales.

It has been discovered that houses in Cornwall, and several other areas, have very high levels of radon compared with the average, and that their inhabitants might therefore be at greater risk of contracting cancer.

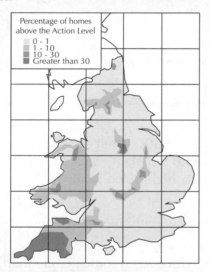

The ground underneath the houses of Cornwall consists of huge deposits of granite. These contain uranium particles, which are radioactive and slowly decaying. One of the products is the radioactive gas, radon, that finds its way through the rocks into homes.

Radon gas gives off alpha radiation as it decays. Alpha radiation is only dangerous over short distances, but if the radon gas is breathed in, the radiation attacks the lining of the lungs and can cause cancer.

There is a direct correlation between deaths due to lung cancer and radon levels. The effect is especially marked in smokers.

All homes in the UK will have some radon gas in them, and it accounts for about half the background radiation we receive. The average radiation from radon in homes is 20 becquerels/cubic metre, but if the level is above 200 Bq/m^3 — the 'action level' — action needs to be taken to reduce it. Someone who lives their whole life in a home at the action level has a greatly increased chance of contracting lung cancer.

Fortunately there is a fairly simple way to protect homes from radon. It involves fitting a 'radon sump' to a property to vent the gas into the atmosphere. A sump has a pipe connecting a space under a solid floor to the outside. A small electric fan in the pipe continually sucks the radon from under the house and pumps it harmlessly into the atmosphere. The cost is a few hundred pounds and grants are available from your local heath authority. New homes can also be protected by building a radon-proof membrane into the floor of the house.

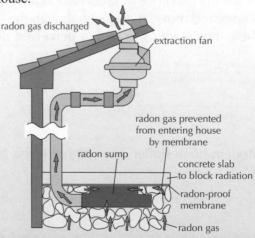

Testing kits to measure the radon levels in homes are available from the Health Protection Agency for about £40.

Radiation and Risk

a) i) Describe which areas on the map show **higher** than average radon levels.

Southewest, most of nodes

ii) What **health problems** would you expect to be more common in these areas?

lung cancer

b) Why are radon levels **different** in different parts of the country?

because the underlying rocks are different

c) Radon gives off **alpha radiation**. Explain how alpha radiation can **damage** the body if it enters it.

It ionises molecules in the cell.

d) Suggest why radon might cause **lung cancer** rather than **other** types of cancer?

& gas is localised in the lungs

e) The danger of radon in homes was only discovered in the 1980s, when a worker in a nuclear plant set off the radiation detectors on his way **into** the plant. Suggest why he didn't know until then that his home had a particularly high radon level.

Radon is invisible

f) When the presence of radon in Cornish homes was first discovered some people tried to **sell** their homes and move away, even though the levels in many of the houses were **below** the **action level**. Were they reacting to **real** or **perceived** risk? Explain your answer.

FOR SALE

g) Modern homes often have **higher** levels of radon than old houses. Suggest a reason for this.

h) i) Give **two** radon protection measures shown in the household protection system on the previous page.

ii) The metal pipe that carries radon gas away passes **through** the house. Why is this still safe, despite radon giving off radiation?

Electricity

Q1 Electricity is a **secondary** energy source. Coal is a **primary** energy source.

a) What does the word 'secondary' mean in this context?

It is made from another energy Source

b) How is electricity **transmitted** from power stations to users in other parts of the country?

National grid.

c) Why is electricity a very **convenient** energy source?

It is easy to Transmit

Q2 The flow chart below shows the main steps in the production of electricity from gas. Use some of the words in blue to fill in the gaps.

| potential | turbine | generator | motor | steam | burned | kinetic |

Gas is *burned* to release energy. ⟹ The energy is used to produce *steam* from water. ⟹ The steam is used to turn a *turbine*. ⟹ The movement (*Kinetic* energy) is converted into electricity by a *generator*.

Q3 In a coal fired power station, **36%** of the energy provided by the coal is converted into useful electrical energy.

a) Suggest **two** ways in which energy is **lost** inside a coal fired power station.

heat and sound energy

b) How much useful **electrical energy** would you get from this power station for each **1000 J** of energy in the coal?

360 J

Q4 Below is a **Sankey diagram** for a **gas fired** power station.

a) What does the **thickness** of the arrows tell you.

the amount of energy that is represents

1000 J input energy from gas

600 J useful electrical energy in the home

322 J heat   50 J noise   28 J heat in wire

b) What **percentage** of the energy supplied by the gas is converted into useful electrical energy?

60%

c) In what **form** is the most energy lost? *heat*

120

Generating Electricity

Q1 **Fossil fuels** (like coal) and **nuclear fuels** (like uranium) are **non-renewable** fuels.

a) What does **non-renewable** mean?

they will run out

b) Name two non-renewable fuels (other than coal and uranium).

Oil, petrol

Q2 The Government has a target to generate **10%** of our electricity from **renewable** resources by **2010**.

a) What do we mean by **renewable resources**?

Ones that can be replaced.

b) Why does generating electricity from renewable resources normally **damage** the environment **less** than using fossil fuels?

much less

Q3 a) Tick the boxes to indicate whether the following resources are renewable or non-renewable.

	Renewable	Non-renewable
i) Solar	✓	
ii) Wind	✓	
iii) Biomass	✓	
iv) Natural gas		✓
v) Geothermal	✓	

b) Name two renewable resources that are only useful in **some places**, and briefly explain why.

Resource: *wind*

Reason: *Turbines need to be situated in windy areas*

Resource: *geothermal*

Reason: *only few countries*

Q4 Underline any statements that are correct.

Solar cells produce electricity using the heat from the Sun.

Solar cells only work in hot countries.

Solar cells are useful for appliances that don't need much energy.

Solar cells use materials like silicon to convert light energy into electricity.

Solar cells have no fuel costs and don't produce carbon dioxide.

Module P3 — Radioactive Materials

Electricity from Nuclear Fuels

Q1 Complete the following passage using appropriate words from the grey box. You may need to use some of the words more than once.

> electrons   split   uranium   fission
>
> neutrons   kerosene   equal   protons   nuclei

A nuclear fuel such as ....*uranium*.... releases large amounts of

energy when its nuclei ....*split*.... . In nuclear

....*fission*...., neutrons are fired at the ....*uranium*....,

causing some of its ....*nuclei*.... to split into two smaller

nuclei, roughly ....*equal*.... in size. The split also releases

two or three more ....*neutrons*.... .

Q2 Which of these statements are **true** and which are **false**?

	True	False
a) In a nuclear power station the uranium is contained in fuel rods.	☐	☐
b) 1 g of uranium releases 10 000 times more energy than 1 g of oil being burnt.	☑	☐
c) Nuclear reactions release a similar amount of energy to chemical reactions.	☐	☑

Q3 Match up the two halves of these statements.

Control rods are used to...

Coolants such as water and CO_2...

In nuclear reactors...

A neutron splits a uranium...

The neutrons released go on...

The chain reaction has to be...

...are used to carry away the heat.

...atom releasing more neutrons.

...controlled to prevent overheating.

...to split more atoms, releasing more neutrons.

...absorb some neutrons.

...a chain reaction is set up.

Top Tips: Nuclear fuel can provide **millions** of times more energy than the same mass of fossil fuel. Given the current concerns about CO_2 emissions from burning fossil fuels, you can see why many people see nuclear fuel as an attractive alternative. Nuclear waste is really **dangerous** though.

Module P3 — Radioactive Materials

Electricity from Nuclear Fuels

Q4   Is the method of **electricity** generation in a **nuclear** power station any different from the method of electricity generation in a **coal-fired** power station? Explain your answer.

....

....

Q5   **Nuclear power stations** produce **radioactive waste** that is difficult to dispose of. Some people believe this makes nuclear power an **unsustainable** technology. Circle the correct word in each of the following sentences.

a)   Clothing that has been used by nuclear technicians is an example of **low** / **intermediate** / **high** level waste.

b)   A lot of heat is generated by **low** / **intermediate** / **high** level waste.

c)   The casing of fuel rods is an example of **low** / **intermediate** / **high** level waste.

d)   **Low** / **Intermediate** / **High** level waste is sealed into concrete blocks and put into steel cans.

e)   **Low** / **Intermediate** / **High** level waste is sealed into glass and steel and allowed to cool for 50 years before permanent storage.

f)   **Low** / **Intermediate** / **High** level waste is buried in secure landfill sites.

Q6   **Storing radioactive waste** is one of the biggest problems that the nuclear industry has. The most likely solution will be **underground** storage.

a)   The site chosen has to be **geologically stable**. What does this mean and why is it important?

....

....

b)   Even geologically stable sites are often **unlikely** to be used for storage. Explain why.

....

c)   Where is most intermediate and high level nuclear waste currently stored?

....

d)   The rules about storage of radioactive waste are very **strict**. Why might they change in the future?

....

e)   Why is the storage of radioactive waste a problem that will be with us for a **very long time**?

....

Electricity in the Future

Q1   Read the passage below and answer the questions that follow.

Is Nuclear the Way to Go?

Our world relies on electricity as a convenient way to run almost every household and business appliance you could think of — from hairdriers to personal computers.

Current methods of generating electricity rely heavily on burning fossil fuels as their primary energy source. But this is not sustainable for two reasons. Firstly, the supply of these fuels is limited and rapidly diminishing. Secondly, the carbon dioxide released when fossil fuels are burnt is having a major effect on the Earth's climate.

The two options, if we want to go on using electricity as we currently do, are to use renewable energy sources, such as wind power, or to use nuclear power.

The Government is seriously thinking of building more new nuclear power stations in a bid to reduce the country's carbon dioxide emissions. At the same time several large-scale wind farms are being proposed at various sites around the UK.

There have been several public enquiries into the siting of wind farms and the arguments have revolved around the potential benefits of wind energy versus the environmental drawbacks.

Those in favour of the wind farms have argued that being able to produce electricity sustainably, and not generating carbon dioxide, far outweighs any other environmental harm they do.

Those against the proposals have argued that the wind turbines would cause visual pollution — they are usually to be sited in the most beautiful areas of the country, such as the Lake District. They also have concerns about the effect on migrating birds and the noise pollution caused by the rotating blades.

New nuclear power stations have not yet reached the public enquiry stage. The arguments are likely to be about the benefits of producing electricity without carbon dioxide emissions against the safety concerns of the local population and the problem of waste disposal. Another factor is the time it will take to build the nuclear power stations compared with the time needed to set up wind farms.

	Wind	Nuclear
CO$_2$ emissions per unit electricity produced (g)	0	110 (due to uranium mining, transport and processing)
Build time (including planning consent)	3-4 years	10-15 years
Lifetime of site (years)	25	25
Cost of energy per unit electricity produced	3-4p	4-7p
Decommissioning cost	Relatively low	Very high
Typical output of power station / farm	60 MW (enough for 40,000 homes)	1200 MW (enough for 800,000 homes)

Electricity in the Future

a) Give two reasons why we'll need to **change** the way we **generate** most of our **electricity** in the future.

1. *Many fossil fuels will run out*
2. *CO₂ emission must be reduces*

b) A **unit of electricity** is enough to run **ten** 100 W light bulbs for an **hour**.

  i) How much carbon dioxide would nuclear power give off in generating enough electricity to run **one bulb** for an **hour**?

    11g

  ii) Coal-fired power stations release about **eight times** as much carbon dioxide for the same amount of electricity produced. How much carbon dioxide would be released from a coal-fired power station in generating enough power to run **one bulb** for an **hour**?

    88g

c) Outline the arguments that **local people** might put forward...

  i) **against** a **wind** farm in their area.

    Visual pollution

  ii) **for** a **nuclear** power station in their area.

    Jobs for contractor building the power station

d) Assuming nuclear power stations can be operated safely, what is the biggest **long-term** problem associated with nuclear power?

  waste disposal

e) How many wind farms would be needed to produce as much electricity as one nuclear power plant?

  1200 ÷ 60 = 20

f) If the **demand** for electricity was expected to rise significantly over the next five years, would it be more sensible to start building wind farms or nuclear power stations? Explain your answer.

  wind farms. B quicker and cheap

g) Why is the **energy output** of a wind farm **less reliable** than that of a nuclear power station?

h) **i)** Why does the wind farm have a **limited lifetime**?

    It contains moving parts

  ii) Suggest why it would be **cheaper** to extend a wind farm's lifetime than a nuclear power station's.

Module P3 — Radioactive Materials